ASHLEY CHASE
A Dorset Domain

To Estelle and Sydney Silverstone
with best wishes
Colette Littman.

Louis Littman by Jeffrey Courtney

ASHLEY CHASE
A Dorset Domain

L.T.S. LITTMAN

ALAN SUTTON
1988

ALAN SUTTON PUBLISHING
BRUNSWICK ROAD · GLOUCESTER

First published 1988

British Library Cataloguing in Publication Data

Littman, L.T.S. (Louis T.S.)
Ashley Chase : a Dorset domain.
1. Dorset. Agricultural industries.
Dairy farms. Management
I. Title
636.2'142

ISBN 0-86299-510-8

Jacket photographs: Sunset over the Bride Valley seen from
Tennants Hill; Summer sunrise from the pavilion. Photographs:
Tim Hawkins

Photographs by Tim Hawkins
Typesetting and origination by
Alan Sutton Publishing Limited
Printed in Great Britain

Contents

Acknowledgements

I wish to thank all those who have helped to give this book its final aspect, one I am sure my husband would have wanted had he lived to see its publication. The author is no longer here to perfect and finish his creation, so the work has had to be done for him. Difficulties inevitably arise when working for someone who alas can no longer indicate what he wants, when every word almost acquires a special importance, and this gives a moral responsibility to ensure that the spirit of his words is maintained.

No one could have helped more than Jeffrey Simmons, the expert leader of our little team, whose advice and support were invaluable; or than Tim Hawkins, whose overall artistic concept resulted in his photographs complementing the text with a beautiful visual image. I must also particularly thank Richard Goddard and Cat Martin, through whose spendidly drawn maps Ashley Chase has somehow acquired a definable geographical and lasting reality.

Colette Littman

Foreword

My husband, Louis Littman, died on 7 December 1987 after he had completed this book. Sadly, he did not live to see its publication, to which he was greatly looking forward. The writing was for him a labour of love and the book appears exactly as he would have wished.

He was, above all, a great romantic, a challenging knight defying adversity. He was also a practical man steeped in many aspects of life, whose sense of business brought about the realization of a dream. There was in him a peculiar and touching blend of realism, which prompted him to deepen his involvement in every aspect of country and farming life, as well as a measure of dreams which gave his achievements a greater dimension. His love of nature was rooted in his instinct for life, in a strong feel for the land, in a sense of responsibility towards it and those it supports. In this respect and to my mind, he shared with the great empire-builders, the consolidators of the past, a mystical sense of the earth, the symbol of basic life and divine creation. He would marvel at a flower or at a shaft of sunlight layered by mist, just as he would marvel at a tractor or at a perfected piece of farm machinery. He saw no difference between them; for him they were different aspects of the same thing.

His love of nature went back to the days when, as a young and sensitive child, he went to a boarding school in Brighton where, for the first time, he discovered and responded to the beauty of the Downs overlooking the sea. This deep emotional experience influenced ever afterwards his wish to succeed in his farming enterprise, an entirely new field, and motivated him to search and find in West Dorset a similar loved landscape.

I owe him an enormous debt of gratitude, for he showed me a greater world of peace and beauty. For me and for all those mentioned in this book, who have witnessed Louis battling undeterred against apathy and incomprehension, led by his vision and by a deep love for his country, his frail silhouette, his brave gentle soul will haunt forever the flowery lanes bordering the meadows, the secret groves carpeted with bluebells, the rounded Downs like great frozen waves protecting paradise.

Colette Littman

CHAPTER *1*

A Boyhood Dream

I suppose that most people nurture a desire to have a realm wholly their own from which they can exclude forces, ideas, people and things they deem ugly, hostile or merely unpleasant; a place they can rule and within which they can create for themselves an atmosphere of beauty, order and tranquillity.

For many this place is their own home, and it depends on their means and their chosen way of life whether this home is a flat in town, a suburban house with a fenced garden, a country cottage, a town mansion or a country estate. In earlier times, and for a few, ambition could raise such desires to encompass a feudal fiefdom, or even a principality. Later on this drive would lead to the creation of vast estates in America or Southern Africa.

The story I am going to tell lies midway between the ordinary and the impossible. It is an account of the way a farming estate of about 2,750 acres was formed, bit by bit, in the loveliest corner of Dorset at an unpropitious time out of unpromising elements, to become eventually the largest dairying estate in the county. It was made possible by the work and devotion of many people, but its driving force was ambition, vision and love.

The first step was made possible through the inheritance from my father of a property empire built up by him, heavily taxed by estate duties, subsequently greatly enlarged by me, and eventually

1

shared with a large family. It left me in 1966, at the age of forty, and for the first and only time in my life, with a large sum of money and no debts.

It sounds a favourable position to find oneself in, but at that time in England there were several factors which somewhat mitigated the apparently delightful prospect of a life of ease and security underpinned by a large sum of money at the bank.

An even stronger reason prevented me from taking the course that some of my family and so many others had done: quite simply, I could not bear the thought of leaving England. Not that I had not often done so. Innumerable holidays had been spent in the historic cities and beautiful coasts and mountains of France, Spain, Portugal, Italy, Greece and Switzerland during the loveliest months of the year. Yet, invariably, after about a month away, came that wave of homesickness, that desire to be back home in England.

It was not that I was wildly jingoistic about my country, affecting to see it superior to any other in all the things that mattered. On the contrary, I knew only too well that it was distinctly inferior to many, not least in its government, and in the spirit of decline and envy that was then rife. It was simply the place where my language was spoken, its literature known, and every nuance of my speech and thought understood. It was the country whose people I liked and the place where I lived and worked, and where I had my niche. It was the country whose ancient towns and delightful villages I had roamed in for many years, imbibing their history, and their atmosphere. Above all, it was where the most civilized, varied and delightful countryside existed, a unique blend of man and nature in a balance and beauty that changed with the seasons but rarely lost its harmony and loveliness.

A Boyhood Dream

I was not going to be driven from all that if I could help it. I acknowledged to myself that if a Nazi or Marxist government seized power and made civilized life, or living at all, impossible I would have a duty to my family to get them away while it was still possible. But I was determined that nothing short of that kind of national catastrophe would send me into exile. I would take my chance and fight the best rearguard action I was able to, but stay on in my own country and live the way I wanted to as best I could.

I proceeded to invest most of my liquid capital in the purchase of commercial buildings where there was some possibility for re-development. It was not altogether easy to find buildings and sites of quality to buy, as many people and financial institutions were as aware as I was of the danger of holding too much cash at that time, and the competition was keen. I earmarked some of my capital to buy a farm.

We had had a country house north of Wimborne for some time which we made particular use of in the school holidays. It had served as a base for sailing from Poole Harbour and for exploring the countryside of Dorset, Wiltshire and Hampshire. It had enabled us to become familiar with the agricultural scene, and gradually I had come to want to have a farm of my own in one of these counties. At that time I was reading some of the novels of Thomas Hardy, and had begun to entertain a desire not merely to observe country life as a tourist or week-end visitor might do, but to live it as one who was part of it. I did not envisage buying a big farm, or indeed moving from our country house. I simply thought of a few hundred acres, not too far from our existing house, which could be managed and run from it, and be reasonably viable as an economic unit.

So I instructed Bernard Thorpe and Partners to look out for something suitable. For a couple of months nothing much happened. Then in March 1966 they said that, in answer to an advertisement they had inserted in *Country Life*, they had received a proposal from the owner of a small estate in West Dorset, and asked if I was prepared to inspect the property. On 26 March, one of their partners from the Wootton Bassett office met me at the Palace Court Hotel in Bournemouth. Reginald Jones was a tall, stately-looking man who had been an officer in the King's African Rifles. He was a building surveyor dealing with country properties. He had once managed the Earl of Suffolk's estate, and found it rather a coincidence that the Countess's maiden name had been the same as my own name. Neither he nor I envisaged at that moment the long connection between us that was just beginning.

We left Bournemouth for Dorchester in sunshine alternating with heavy rain squalls, slipped down to Portesham by the Hardy Monument, and got to Abbotsbury. There we were enveloped in such a thick fog that it was necessary to turn on the fog lamps. We proceeded slowly for about a mile west of the village, going by an Ordnance Survey Map, for we were in what was to us wholly unknown country and could, for all we could see, be on Dartmoor. We were quite unaware that from the top of Wears Hill, to which we drove and which was 700 feet above the sea, one of the most splendid panoramas on the south coast, embracing Lyme Bay from Portland Bill to Tor Bay, could normally be seen, for we could only see ten yards ahead of us; as we went higher and higher we imagined a rough hill farm with broken-down buildings fit for some sheep, but little else, as our likely destination. At the top of Wears Hill we could just make out a signpost, pointing inland to Ashley Chase. We followed it, passed a massive Iron Age earthwork called Abbotsbury Castle, and gradually entered an isolated valley shielded from the sea by the massive bulk of Wears Hill. As we slowly descended, the mist cleared a little, and we found ourselves amid sheep pastures in apparently good heart with multitudes of healthy-looking sheep grazing them. The fields seemed well fenced and everything had a well-kept look. Reg Jones was suitably impressed.

The particulars we had been given referred to an estate of 680 acres having four cottages and a stone house. The latter description conjured up a picture of something large, gaunt, Victorian and rather unmanageable. We edged along, passed some coppices and came to a group of houses among some trees in a hollow. We took them for the stone house and cottages until we saw, about 200 yards to the east, in the thinning mist, a very large, very well-built house in seventeenth-century Cotswold style. Our first thought was that it must be a neighbouring property, but a further glance at the Ordnance Survey Map assured us that it was on the estate. So we drove up to it and the nearer we got the greater grew our sense of wonder. This was no shabby, run-down Victorian house as we had expected, but a splendid stone-clad manor house with golden Hamstone mullions, and a greenish roof of Cornish Delabole slate. It presented a varied facade, full of gables, stone chimneys, projecting wings, and even a round tower capped with a bronze weather-vane in the form of a galleon.

The owner, a huge man of six foot seven, came out to meet us, stooping as he did so as to clear the gothic-shaped lintel to the front door. Russell Wood had farmed some 3,000 acres in Hertfordshire before coming down to Dorset about twelve years before to live in semi-retirement. He had become an expert on Dorset Down sheep, which had the advantage of lambing whenever one wanted them to, and therefore at Christmas time so as to be ready for the lucrative Spring market, and there were plenty of them scattered among the more numerous Scots half-bred on the adjacent hills. He showed us into the spacious oak-panelled hall. Through the leaded windows I could see a garden terrace and a rather tangled

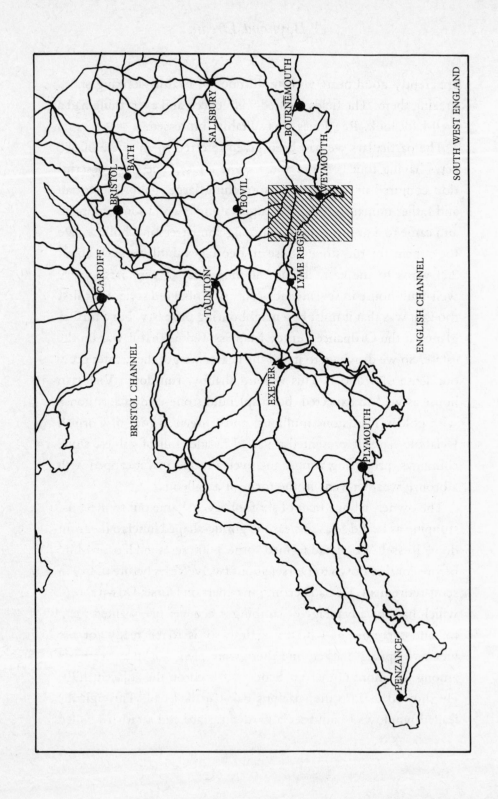

BOURNEMOUTH

SALISBURY

WEYMOUTH

BATH

YEOVIL

BRISTOL

LYME REGIS

CARDIFF

TAUNTON

BRISTOL CHANNEL

ENGLISH CHANNEL

EXETER

PLYMOUTH

PENZANCE

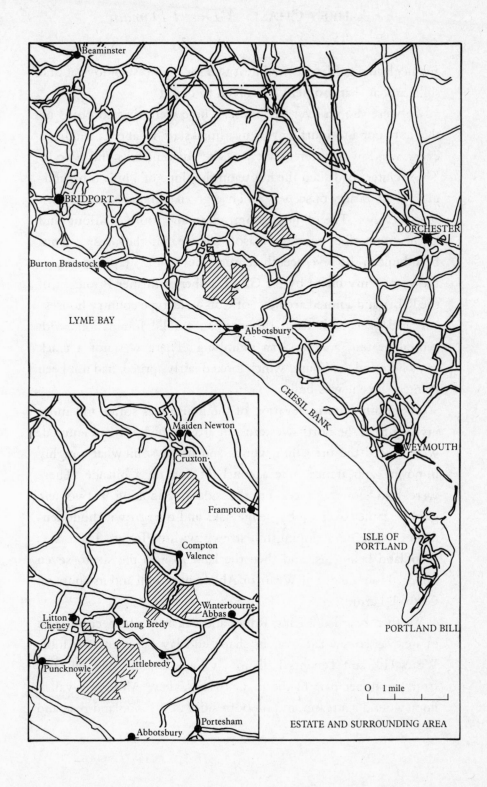

Beaminster

BRIDPORT

Burton Bradstock

LYME BAY

Abbotsbury

CHESIL BANK

DORCHESTER

WEYMOUTH

ISLE OF
PORTLAND

PORTLAND BILL

Maiden Newton

Cruxton

Frampton

Compton
Valence

Winterbourne
Abbas

Litton
Cheney

Long Bredy

Littlebredy

Pucknowle

Portesham

Abbotsbury

O   1 mile

ESTATE AND SURROUNDING AREA

and neglected garden beyond it. It was for me a case of love at first sight and at that moment I resolved to buy it.

We were shown over the house. There were six bedrooms on the first floor and a further two in a small staff flat above, and from every window a different view of the adjacent hills and woods. The architect had sited the house on the slope of a hill commanding a great variety of scenery and had given each bedroom its own special view. The dining room, drawing room, parlour and kitchen were all of good but reasonable size, and the house had not been built in the seventeenth century, but in 1925 (appropriately, the year of my birth) by Sir Guy Dawber, a former President of the RIBA and a noted architect of Cotswold-type country houses.

It had been built from the start on a solid foundation, with central heating and modern plumbing. There was not a crack anywhere and the house, which looked fairly spruce, had not been painted since it was built.

The south-eastern elevation of the house was softer and more inviting than the north-western side from which we had entered, which faced the prevailing winds and had a somewhat roughly imposing appearance, like a couchant lion on a hillside. There were two stone terraces on the side overlooking a two-acre garden, rather overrun by hedge oaks and overgrown rhododendron bushes, on a sloping hill strewn with daffodils. There was woodland below us, and then the land rose to the six to seven hundred foot height of Wears or Abbotsbury Hill and its spurs on Gorwell Farm.

We then boarded a Land Rover and began our inspection. The estate was somewhat oval in shape and lay between two hills, Wears Hill and Tenants Hill, in a valley running obliquely out from the upper part of the main Bride Valley. Along the valley floor wound a stream, and on both sides of it woodland rose and

Summer sunrise from the pavilion

View from Abbotsbury Hill. St Catherine's Chapel stands alone in the foreground overlooking the Chesil Bank and the Isle of Portland

The building of Ashley Chase house

Blossom in the garden

covered the lower slopes of the hills. These wooded slopes had a primaeval look about them and probably were much the same mixture of ash, oak and alder as in the time of the Ancient Britons.

The builder of the house had been Sir David Milne-Watson, a Scots solicitor, who had been chairman of the Southern Gas, Light and Coke Company. He had purchased Ashley Chase, which then included Gorwell Farm and amounted to over 1,200 acres, as a rough shooting estate, and had kept it that way. The woods teemed with deer, pheasant, woodcock, hares and rabbits. Buzzards soared high above the woods and kestrels could be seen hovering overhead.

Russell Wood took us halfway up the southern flank of Tenants Hill, from where we could look down the eight-mile length of the Bride Valley to Golden Cap, the gold sandstone cliff reputed to be the highest on the south coast, and beyond it to the sea to Lyme Regis. This was part of the coastal scenery described by Ralph Wightman in his delightful book *Portrait of Dorset*, where he writes:

East of Burton Bradstock one road runs up the Bride Valley and the other skirts the coast over the coastal ridge. The best way to follow this road is westward into the sunset from the top of Abbotsbury Hill. From here the great cliffs of the Bridport-Lyme Regis region merge with the Devon coast as far as Start Point. There are amazing colours, curious lights and shadows, veils of mist which leave Golden Cap floating insubstantial as a dream island. It is Merlin's magic earth, a precious stone, the walls of England and the fields of home.

For me the curious thing was that although I had travelled over most of Dorset, I could not recall ever having seen this secluded and beautiful valley.

Russell Wood returned with us to the house. He told us that, apart from some desultory farming during the war, the estate had been a wild rabbit warren. With the aid of government grants, often amounting to 100 per cent of the cost, he had drained most of the unwooded land. He had then fenced it and turned it into a sheep ranch carrying 800 ewes with their lambs. He had a staff of four who did shepherds' work without exactly being skilled shepherds. Some of them helped in the house, and I gathered that he was afraid of telling them that he was going to sell for fear they would leave him before he had done so. I subsequently learned that the property had been quietly on offer for about two years but had found no buyer as yet, partly because of its remoteness, and partly because the hilly nature of the country was deemed to prevent it from being ploughed or used for serious dairying. But for me such considerations lay in the future. What I saw before me was a delightful house in the midst of superbly beautiful and varied countryside, a glorious place in which to live and to run a moderate farming enterprise.

I asked the price. Russell Wood said '£120,000', adding rather apologetically that he had added £10,000 to the price of the estate because of the house, which was rather grander than the usual farmhouse. I then asked him if he had children who might want to keep the place, not being able to understand how, if he had any, they could allow such a lovely estate to be sold. He replied that he had a son and daughter and that neither was interested in it. I suppose I could have bargained, but the price seemed reasonable, and I did not want to run the slightest risk of losing what I had found. Russell Wood had just let 100 acres of the woodlands to the Forestry Commission for a negligible rent, and considered it a good deal since they would be responsible for replanting it, while he retained the sporting rights and could presumably use any road they would build. His asking price therefore worked out at £176 an acre including the leased woodland, and £207 an acre excluding it. If one considered that the whole estate contained over 150 acres of woodland, and that good farmland adjacent to it fetched between £220 and £250 an acre, he was asking a fairly full price, but I did not hesitate for a moment. I shook hands at £120,000 there and then, and left in a mood of suppressed exultation. I had agreed to buy a little realm of my own, over a square mile in extent, with a dream of a house, for a few symbols on a piece of paper.

Passing through the village of Puncknowle, a little to the west of the estate, I saw a telephone box and decided to tell my wife of my decision. She already had a sixteen-room house in Kensington to look after and was not relishing the task of taking on another large residence. Besides, she was very fond of our nine-room country cottage, as we all were. So I told her that I had agreed to buy the estate, which was situated in superb countryside near the sea. 'Is there a house on it?' I was asked. 'Yes, a lovely one,' I said. 'Is it big?' All things are relative. By some standards it was not big, by others it might have been considered so. It had in fact about as many rooms as our London house, but it looked larger, as most of the rooms were laid out on two floors instead of four and a couple of half-landings. So I was a little non-committal on this point, merely saying that it was delightful and that she was bound to love it.

The next day I drove Colette and my elder son, Robbie, then thirteen years old, to see it. A good impression was made and Robbie was, in fact, quite excited.

On 30 March, Reg Jones rang to say that Russell Wood agreed to sell at his asking price. On 27 April contracts were exchanged.

Ever since my boyhood I had dreamed of one day acquiring an

agricultural estate. I had always placed it in hilly country like the South Downs in Sussex, near which I went to school, and over which I used to roam. By the time I was thirty-five I thought I might be able to realize this dream by the time I was fifty, and that if nothing suitable then turned up, I might even build a country house. Now, at forty, I had my estate and my country house, not it was true in the Sussex Downs, but in a county more remote, more unspoiled, with the same features of bare chalk hills, sheltered coombes with wooded valleys, and far-ranging views over the sea.

The deepest sense of satisfaction comes to us when dreams of childhood are fulfilled. This particular dream had been one of mine.

CHAPTER 2

Establishing Ourselves

We were not due to complete the purchase until July, but there was an enormous amount to think of and to do. Any ideas I had about farming were rudimentary in the extreme. Richard Thorpe, who had read Agriculture at Trinity College, Cambridge a little after I had read Law there, was ready to act as my land agent. But I needed a skilled and reliable manager, particularly as I only intended to live for part of the year on the estate.

One day late in May he introduced me to John Thacker, a Suffolk man who had been managing farm estates since he was twenty-three. He had spent the previous ten years running an 800-acre estate near Guildford for the Guthrie Corporation, which made a speciality of buying estates, developing them, and then selling them, often piecemeal. It had recently sold the estate he was managing and he was now out of a job. There he was, a man of middle height, robust health and open countenance, looking for a new managerial position and, as he told me much later, expecting a situation of semi-retirement in the job that Richard Thorpe had outlined to him. I liked him and felt a trust in him at once. I imagine that this interview, which took place over lunch at the Reform Club and lasted four hours, changed his life as much as it did mine. He had a wife, Joan, and five children, three of whom lived with him: Ian, then aged seventeen, who was a stockman, and two girls, Jane and Wendy. Terms were soon arranged. He would come as manager and head shepherd at a salary of £1,500 a year with a cottage and free heating. The rest of the interview was devoted to Scots half-bred sheep, fleeces, mutton, cattle, grass, hay, rivers, fish, and wild life in general. He did not know Dorset at all, and I gave him some outline of the countryside there with its towns and villages.

By that time we had made several exploratory excursions into the Bride Valley and the adjacent coast. The Bride Valley villages, Litton Cheney, Long Bredy, Littlebredy and Puncknowle, nestling at the foot or on the flanks of the Downs, with their mediaeval churches, stone cottages and neat gardens, were delightful and looked as if they had not changed much since the eighteenth century.

Even from their vantage points Ashley Chase, when it could be seen at all, looked like a remote, half-wild tract of upland, and its house, when seen, isolated and hidden away. There was nothing in that valley then which would have seemed incongruous in an eighteenth-century landscape. It was a masterpiece of the harmony which can be attained when men see to it that their handiwork blends with their natural surroundings. The whole valley seemed to be, as if under a spell, in a timeless past unaffected by wars, the scars of industrial development and the trauma of social upheaval.

It was a paradise but, as we soon discovered, even a paradise could be improved. We had agreed with Russell Wood that he and his wife could stay on at the house until the end of August, when their new house would be ready. But we visited the estate frequently, and on one occasion had tea with the Russell Woods in the hall of the house. That was the intention anyway, although when we saw the colour of the water being poured into the teapot, we agreed that it might be safer for my wife and me to have tonic water instead. The water was the colour of cocoa: we soon learned why. It came from a stream about 150 yards below the house from which it was drawn by a Heath Robinson contraption involving a pump and a water ram. This not infrequently broke down, and when it did, it required the personal exertions of Russell Wood, who might have to venture into the woods at night or in the rain, before a bath could be had or a cup of tea be drunk. The brownish colour of the water was caused by the presence of iron in the stream bed, and we learned that iron had actually been mined to the north of Wears Hill in the last century. I did not find the idea of drinking surface water contaminated by sheep droppings and fertilizer very attractive and, for about a year, whenever we visited Ashley Chase we took our own drinking water with us, as if on an African safari.

I completed the purchase of the estate on 5 July 1966, taking over about 800 ewes and their progeny. Two of Russell Wood's shepherds were taken on as well. Over the next two years I assembled a group of advisers and contractors to assist in carrying out the tasks facing us. There were two objectives. The first revolved round the house and garden, which I had to turn into a home that would be attractive to my wife and children. The second centred on raising the farming potentiality of the estate. I encountered many problems I had not foreseen in both fields, but pressed on to remedy them simultaneously.

It soon became clear that the house needed attention, while the garden, which had been planted with rare trees, an abundance of rhododendrons and daffodils and some camellias and azaleas on an

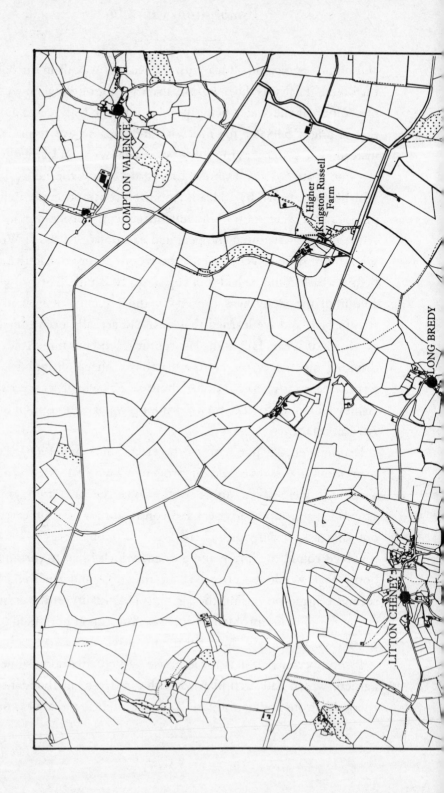

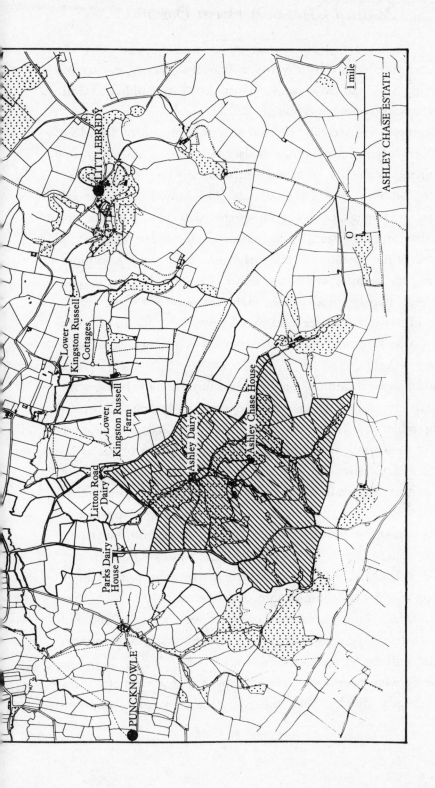

LITTLEBREDY

Lower
Kingston Russell
Cottages

Lower
Kingston Russell
Farm

Ashley Dairy

Litton Road
Dairy

Ashley Chase House

Ashley Dairy

Parks Dairy
House

PUNCKNOWLE

ASHLEY CHASE ESTATE

1 mile

attractive sloping site by the Milne-Watsons, was in danger of becoming a jungle. So a team was gradually assembled to deal with the improvements required.

I had met Brian Metcalfe Jackson in Wimborne where he had an attractive seventeenth-century house and ran an antique shop specializing in the sale of seventeenth-century English furniture, Chinese ceramics and Oriental rugs. His knowledge of those subjects was encyclopaedic. He prepared a plan for the re-decoration and furnishing of the house. We decided to furnish it in the style of the seventeenth and early eighteenth century, as most befitting the architecture of the house. Our London house was furnished largely with late eighteenth-century and early nineteenth-century pieces and we knew correspondingly less about earlier furniture. So this decision led us into new sources of aesthetic delight.

Within eighteen months or so we had furnished the house with Jacobean chests and chairs, early Georgian desks, mid-Georgian dining table and chairs, seventeenth-century oak and walnut furniture and some exotic Spanish and Italian pieces of the same epoch, with Persian, Turkish and Caucasian rugs to add colour and comfort. The walls of the bedrooms and the corridors on that floor were grey, accentuating the somewhat monastic appearance of that part of the house, which relied for interest on the strong colours of the curtains, bedcovers and rugs. The ground floor was treated differently, each room with its own appropriate colour scheme: blue for the dining room, blue and white *toile de jouy* for the breakfast room, Japanese rice-paper for the study and red Jacobean-patterned wallpapers for the lobbies, while the colours in the kitchen were white and yellow.

The drawing room was given exceptional treatment. Its walls were already divided into thirteen panels by super-imposed wooden frames, and Metcalfe Jackson thought it a good idea to have these fitted with wallpaper made in mainland China with genuine Chinese decorations, rather than with the European motifs made in China for the European market for the previous three centuries. He found at Collett's, a Chinese-owned shop then opposite the British Museum, a willingness to work with him. He produced an outline of the design over thirteen panels of different shapes and sizes. Once I had agreed to it, the panels were meticulously measured by him and the order, together with the measurements, despatched to China. Within about two months we were notified that the papers had arrived at the London docks. Unfortunately a dock strike was in progress, and it took longer for them to journey from London to Dorset than from China to London. When they finally arrived, we all gathered around with a sense of anticipatory trepidation. The consignment was unrolled, and there on a background of pale apricot-coloured paper-backed silk was a series of delightful paintings of budding cherry blossoms, ferns, birds, ducks and butterflies. It fitted the panels perfectly.

Metcalfe Jackson then designed the curtains and pelmets for the three windows of this room, so open to the sun and air. We were somewhat dumbfounded when we eventually saw them hanging, for the curtains were of golden wild silk while their pelmets were pink, trimmed with dark green silk braid and tassels of the same colour. Moreover, these pelmets were pointed at each end to resemble the corners of a Chinese pagoda. Pink and gold in juxtaposition is not a colour combination common in Europe, but once we had got over our surprise, we were delighted with its beauty and originality, and dubbed the style 'Classic Mongol'.

Metcalfe Jackson now discovered an old-fashioned iron and brass forge in, of all places, Carnaby Street in London, and they made for us a number of chandeliers, wall sconces and fireplace implements in brass or silvered brass in a variety of Jacobean and Queen Anne styles, some directly copied from those made for Blenheim Palace.

But other matters, even more pressing than the furnishing of the house, required our attention first. The electric wiring had not been touched since the house had been built forty years before. This was quickly replaced by an aluminium conduit system. The central heating pipework had also to be replaced, and for a curious reason: the iron in the water had gradually lined the pipes so that, over the years, their effective diameter had been reduced by half. I could envisage the day when these pipes might be completely blocked, so that now, when the house was empty, was the best time to replace them. With these tasks accomplished, the house could be safely decorated within and without. All these tasks were put into the hands of the small building firm of C.G. Fry and Son of Litton Cheney. Edward Fry ran a small wheelwright and carpentering business that had been carried on by his forebears in the village for generations. He was a very tall, thin, cheerful man, a pillar of the village church and a member of Litton Cheney's Parish Council. He quickly won our confidence and was soon involved in every scheme we set on foot in regard to the house and the estate. His firm grew with the demands made on it, and his two or three carpenters and decorators stretched to thirty or forty as, to the surprise of his old father, he became, with us, the largest employer in the Bride Valley.

The garden posed a further problem. I have likened it to the Garden of Eden, and like that garden it contained serpents. We had been given a hint of this by Mrs Wood when we had come to tea. Addressing herself to Colette, she had said rather airily, 'I hope you don't mind snakes.' Her husband had transfixed her with a quelling look and we heard no more on the subject. It would however have been surprising had the garden, which adjoined acres of woodland and had been allowed to grow wild, been free of snakes. The grass was everywhere five to six feet high, save for a swathe a yard wide, cut into the jungle, along which one could descend to a dell covered with bushes. Rhododendrons grew large and wild. Hedge oaks had spread from the adjacent woodlands, choking the fine trees originally planted by Milne-Watson, and obscuring the views from the house. Drastic action was required, and we took it. A forestry firm was engaged to remove the unwanted trees, and it took them five weeks. Mrs Wood's muted warning was justified. As the tree roots were pulled up, adders and grass-snakes slithered out in every direction. John Thacker said he had never seen so many in his life.

As we grew more familiar with the house, we noticed some quite unnecessary blemishes on the north-west aspect, the direction from which one approached it from the outside world. Fences came up to the very terrace adjoining the house, to prevent sheep coming up to the front door. Telegraph poles and poles carrying electric wires marched, like tall guardsmen, along the meadows to the house, giving it the appearance of a divisional HQ in wartime. I soon decided that both telegraph wires and the Southern Electricity Board's wires would have to dive into the ground 200 yards away, and from there make a surreptitious and underground approach that would not disfigure the house or spoil the view. When the Post Office and Electricity Board heard my suggestions, they were, predictably, difficult and obstructive. It was not usually done, they said, and if it were done it would be costly, and so on. I could not allow such poor arguments to prevail over the aesthetic ones. I enquired the cost of redirecting these disfiguring utilities and was, somewhat reluctantly, given it. I paid and the work was done. Both the Post Office and the Electricity Board remained puzzled that anyone should pay good money, £112 for the telephone and £519 for the electric cable, not for practical benefits, but merely to secure an unspoiled view, while I could not imagine money better spent.

It was Eddie Fry who suggested a way of getting rid of the fences near the front of the house. Either we would have to ban sheep and cattle from grazing the twelve acres of pasture in front of the house, which seemed doubly wasteful, for not only would we, in that event, lose the pasturage but we would also have to keep the grass mown; or we could let the sheep graze but build a great ha-ha thirty yards from the house, and crossed only by a cattle grid for vehicles and a wicket gate for pedestrians. A ha-ha is a deep ditch faced on one or both sides by a steeply pitched stone-retaining wall, and its object is to keep cattle out without the intervention of a hedge or wood and wire fencing. A stranger approaching the house is supposed to wonder why the grazing sheep or cattle stop well short of the house without anything visible appearing to prevent their advance to the front door. Could it be that they have been trained to stay a respectful distance from the house? As he himself draws nearer, he sees the stone-faced embankment sunk into the ground, and roars with laughter. Hence the name. We opted for the latter; bulldozers were therefore brought in to level bumpy and irregular fields so that they could be turfed and cut, the ha-ha was dug, and the great house began to change its appearance. From looking somewhat like an abandoned monastery immured in its woods and put to inappropriate use, it began to emerge, decked out in new lawns and cleared of wires and poles, as a small but reasonably stately home.

I was absorbed with the work of improvement and with the

newly encountered agricultural problems, and it was Colette who drew my attention to the needs of the children. They could not be expected to spend day after day merely rounding up sheep or chasing butterflies. Robbie was then thirteen and Cedric eight, and the nearest safe beach was at Weymouth, some twelve miles away. Moreover, it was not very pleasant and could be dangerous to leave them to play in a snake-infested garden. So, through Reg Jones, we were put in touch with John Booth, a landscape gardener. He had been heavily engaged on the lay-out of war cemeteries, had designed the garden for Nubar Gulbenkian's country house in Buckinghamshire, and was about to design the garden which the latter was planning for the great tomb he was building for himself in the south of France.

A company was brought in to build a pool forty feet long and twenty feet wide, with a classical oval shape at either end, to be screened on two sides by protecting lines of cupressus, an idea I derived from La Pietà, Sir Harold Acton's villa outside Florence.

'If the boys are going to have a pool', I said, 'I shall have a tennis court.' It was easier said than done. The designated position for both was below the eastern boundary of the garden, and there was no means of access save through the garden, which would then be virtually wrecked by the heavy earth excavators required. Moreover, there was not a level spot in the garden once one stepped off the terrace, since it was on the fairly steep slope of a hill. And what did one do with the extensive amount of soil dug to make a pool forty feet long, twenty feet wide and nine feet deep at one end? The solution found by John Thacker and Eddie Fry to both problems was to build a new hard-core road about 120 yards long and ten feet wide from the garage side of the house round the north and east boundaries of the garden in a dog-legged shape, on which the heavy earth-moving vehicles could run without wrecking the garden. It turned out a bigger job than was expected, for the soil proved to be a water-logged greensand and it required hard core to a depth of four feet to prevent such machines simply disappearing. The excavated soil from the pool would be used to rear up a great embankment that would buttress the pool from the side which sloped away, and any surplus could be laid on the tennis court which, it was planned, would be carried onto the lower slope of the hill east of the pool.

We then had to consider building a dressing room, for the pool would be seventy yards from the house. At that point, John Booth suggested that we engage an architect to build a gazebo to link up the pool and the tennis court, which were on totally different levels, and recommended a friend of his, John Rouse, who had a practice in Kent. Early in 1968 Rouse came down to look at the site, which then resembled a builder's yard, and to ascertain what we wanted. He had made some tentative drawings and I well remember how he, Colette, John Thacker, Eddie Fry and I assembled in the empty hall before a roaring log-fire one winter's night. Only two of us sat, Colette on a kitchen chair brought from John Thacker's cottage, and I on an upturned log, although it was not long before we all lay on the polished floors in front of the fire, the better to pore over the various sketches spread out before us. We had the choice of an enclosed building of two storeys linking up the two levels and built of Forest Marble to blend with the house, or a pavilion on two floors but open to the winds on the top floor, with its sloping roof held up by arches supported by round columns with Doric capitals springing from a dwarf wall: a style we had encountered in the cloisters of San Marco which houses those lovely paintings of Fra Angelico in Florence.

We could not at first make up our minds. I favoured the enclosed scheme which would, I thought, be more useful, and more in tune with the house. But would it really tie in with the classical lines of the pool? Was not the conception wrong? After all, no one, in late seventeenth- or early eighteenth-century England built swimming pools, classically designed or otherwise, to go with their Cotswold manor houses, and it would be a foolish anachronism to build a dressing room on the assumption that they did. Therefore why not go whole-hog Renaissance and build a Renaissance type of pavilion to face a classically designed pool? I recall that I was in favour of the first solution and Colette the second. The others veered from one to the other. Finally, Colette rose from the hearth and said she was going to bed, leaving us her own rough sketch of the Renaissance building that she favoured.

In the morning we told her that she had won, and we left it to John Rouse to tackle the details of a building that posed difficult problems. It had to form a link between a swimming pool and a tennis court, the latter some twelve feet below the former, and combine modern amenities with a Renaissance style. An original design evolved to meet these difficulties. It certainly had a Renaissance flavour taken as a whole, but the semicircular roof covering the stairway linking the two floors, which was itself contained within an apse-shaped protuberance built out from the one solid free-standing wall that the building possessed, could be said to have affinities with Byzantine architecture.

John Rouse, never having built one before, took no chances with the construction of this Renaissance pavilion. So a solid reinforced concrete shell, strong enough to withstand pressure from three sides of solid earth with a roof solid enough to mount a four-inch gun, formed the base of the airy structure that eventually rose above the higher level. We had to choose what stone to use. I first inclined towards reconstituted stone, on the grounds of cost, but was deflected from what would have been a disastrous choice by a visit with Rouse and Colette to Corsham in Wiltshire in September 1969. There we learned that a superb structure could be built in solid stone, using the skills of stonemasons exercising a traditional art, for considerably less than we had been advised reconstituted stone would cost. Great piles of Doulting, Bath, Guiting and Clipsham lay around us. We finally chose Clipsham, a golden stone like Bath, but with twice its density, which it would need to resist the salt-laden winds blowing in from the sea. When the various sections of stone fabric had been carved, a team of stonemasons arrived and lodged in Abbotsbury while they gradually assembled it. In such a way were stone churches and cathedrals built in the Middle Ages, and this pavilion, as we called it, must have been the first building so erected in Dorset for a generation.

We chose York stone for the floor, and I spent an unusual afternoon with John Rouse in a place I had not known to exist, namely the great delivery yards of St Pancras Station, choosing slabs of York stone for their size and colour. The roof was tiled, like the house, with greenish-tinted Delabole slates from Cornwall. On the lower floor were showers and changing rooms which opened out through glazed doors of cedar wood to a cedar pergola from whose timbers we hoped would one day hang Russian and Virginia vines, clematis, roses and wisteria. It was not finished for two or three years, for the earthen banks and foundations had to be allowed to dry out, and the land to settle. When completed, it turned out to be a thing of wonder whose beauty, reflected in the waters of the pool, evoked, despite a different style of architecture, memories of the Moorish pavilions reflected in the pools of the Alhambra. I rarely saw it without remembering those lines of Coleridge,

> 'In Xanadu did Kubla Khan
> A stately pleasure dome decree . . .'

CHAPTER 3

Preserving the Woodlands

The building of the pavilion was only one of several projects for the garden which we put in hand in those first two or three years. About thirty yards south-west of it lay a dell overrun by bushes, and twenty yards west of that a little stream, hardly larger than an open ditch, but full enough to render the surrounding area a bit of a swamp, in which it simply disappeared underground. I think it was Colette who said, as she one day surveyed this particular corner of the wilderness, 'Why not turn it into a lily pond?' So we did. In came the excavators and out came the bushes. Half the bank forming the dell was broken down and joined with the lawn. Concrete was laid on the bottom and the stream was piped from the point it disappeared, which happened to be under a magnificent Davidia involucrata, or Chinese Handkerchief tree, which has the unusual trick of sporting white leaves in the month of May, and made to cascade down a flight of stone steps into the new pool. Later, a stone path was laid round the circumference of the pool and a great stone vase was placed on a pedestal in its centre, whilst hydrangeas were planted on its steep banks. A timber pergola was put up facing it and goldfish were introduced in the water to swim between the water lilies. There, we thought, with the children playing by our side, the blue and green dragonflies darting here and there on whirring wings, the goldfish cruising lazily, we would dream away the sun-drenched days of summer, mesmerized by the tinkling sound of falling water.

Finally, we had to clear the jungle in order to lay out flower beds. The only way to do that was to smooth out the ground, which was nothing more than a sloping field, and lay turves on it so that it could be regularly mown, and then hope that the vibrations of a heavy mower would effectively banish the serpents from Eden. But who was to do the gardening? It was no use asking farm-workers to do it regularly, for they would object to being transferred from farm work. The problem was solved as a result of an unexpected upheaval over the hill at Kingston Russell House. It had been bought from the Vestey family by John Cordle, then MP for East Bournemouth, soon after we had bought Ashley Chase, but the Cordle family did not stay long in residence and among the employees who lost their jobs were their two gardeners, John and Sid Ellery. These brothers, in their fifties, had, it was believed, never left the Bride Valley; and they felt no deprivation on that account. They had bicycles but never used them to go further than the Valley villages. They had not wished to leave Kingston Russell House and its five acres of garden until necessity compelled them to, but now they came to us. They had to be fetched and returned by car, because pushing a bike up and down Tenants Hill from their house in Long Bredy would have taken them an hour each way. It was tall John and short Sid who, over a period of years, smoothed out and turfed our rough hillside wilderness and turned it into a garden. They eventually left for the reason they had come. A new owner, Sir

Charles Peak, arrived at Kingston Russell House, and they got their old jobs back.

The Ashley Chase woods, from which Ashley Chase estate derived its name, ran for about two miles along the lower slopes of the spurs of Wears Hill and Gorwell to the fields of Parks Farm. In summer they appeared an almost impenetrable thicket in which streams meandered, deer wandered, and birds, rabbits and hares found shelter. They probably had not changed much since Celtic times. No one pretended there was very much good timber there but the overall effect was beautiful, whether one saw them in the leafless days of Winter, the best time for wandering in them, in the delicately variegated light green foliage of Spring, the fullness of Summer, or the gloriously rich tints of Autumn. I do not think there are many woods as unspoiled as these in the whole of Dorset. They were effectively cut in two by the dirt track which crossed the Ashley stream and connected us, after a fashion, via other dirt tracks and lanes, to the road leading to Litton Cheney. There were about ninety acres of woodland to the west of this road, of which fifty-five acres had been leased to the Forestry Commission, and forty-five acres to the east of it, all of which had been leased to them.

Chapel Wood in the western part sheltered the ruined mediaeval chapel of St Luke. There was nothing left of it but an old wall pierced by an arch, but its situation, some sixty feet above two wooded glens, was highly romantic. Such an effect did it have on Sir David and Lady Milne-Watson, who had built the house at Ashley Chase, that they had had the chapel reconsecrated, erected an altar, and arranged for their tombs to be placed in the chapel. The eastern woods effectively screened Ashley Chase house from view, giving it the appearance of a little chateau in the forest, strayed perhaps from the pages of Perrault's Fairy Tales.

ASHLEY CHASE: *A Dorset Domain*

When I bought the estate I did not give much thought to the 100 acres of these woodlands which Russell Wood had leased to the Forestry Commission. There did not seem much I could about it and I had enough on my hands to attend to. Then one day in the Autumn of 1966 I took a walk with Colette over the western part of our new domain. We walked down a hard-core lane, rather vaingloriously called the County Road, which would have led to Parks Farm, adjacent to us, had it not disappeared without trace into the fields. Off it lay a sloping meadow called Lay Hill field which offered glorious views away to the north-west over the Bride Valley and to Pilsden and Lewesdon Hills in the distance, and south-west to Golden Cap and across the sea to Lyme Regis and Dartmoor. We sat in that field and gazed with wonder at our distant surroundings, with feelings of peace and contentment; but as we drew in our gaze, we saw, between us and Puncknowle, a heavy black smudge occupying about seventy acres on the lower fields to the west of us. It looked ugly, like a week-old stubble beard. A dark suspicion crossed my mind. We hurried home and rang up Eddie Fry to ask what he knew about it. The answer came at once. It was the woods of the Puncknowle estate which had been leased to the Forestry Commission, who had made a clear fell of them and replanted with conifers. They had admitted that it might be pretty unsightly for some years, but afterwards there would a fine new forest. What they had not said was that their coniferous plantations introduced an alien feature into the downland landscape, and that the soil on which they were planted would cease to harbour the wild life and vegetation it once enjoyed.

Then I learned that Puncknowle Wood was only a part of what the Forestry Commission hoped would be a South Dorset Forest stretching up to the Hardy Monument on Blackdown Hill, of which Ashley Chase would be the centre. I suddenly realized the fate in store for this valley. Its peace, charm and tranquillity, to which these woods so greatly contributed, would be destroyed and never again restored. It would be turned into a pulp-yard by bulldozers, tractors and trailers. Ashley Chase would be laid bare and the circle of its enchantment destroyed.

I told John Thacker that the bulldozing had to stop. We should tell the forestry workers that we were negotiating with the Forestry Commission and that they should cease work. If they did not, we would cut off their access to the woods. They did stop, partly because of the fuss I made, and partly because the rainy season was approaching, when the road they were making for the purpose of dragging out the old timber would soon be transformed into a quagmire. Negotiations with the Commission for the return of the woodlands began in leisurely fashion and dragged on for two years until in August 1968 Reg Jones told me that my appeal had been rejected.

Then I turned to the public, first to the Council for the Preservation of Rural England and then to the Dorset Naturalists, and told them of the position. They were sympathetic and agreed to help as much as they could. I got journalists in the local press to report on the threatened devastation. We got up a petition, which attracted over eight hundred signatures, to save Ashley Chase Woods. I well remember Colette sitting on a chair in front of a trestle table with a banner behind her at the Melplash and Dorchester Shows, alongside huge tractors and earth-movers. It would be encouraging for public involvement in protection of the environment to be able to record that all this public interest had an effect on the Forestry Commission, but it did not. The only thing that really acted like a brake on them was my own stubbornness, backed up by threats of a thoroughly non-legal nature. Neither our neighbour Colonel Wordsworth, Chairman of the Dorchester Bench, nor John Thacker thought I had a chance of stopping them once they had summoned up the will to act.

Indeed the odds were heavily against me. The Forestry Commission, a State Corporation owning or leasing millions of acres throughout the country with thousands of men under its command and a hefty annual subsidy from government of around £250,000,000, was a mighty organization and in high favour with government and public opinion at that time. They would point to the vast areas of the Scottish Highlands they had reafforested, the timber-based industries they had encouraged and the employment they gave to thousands of people, and they basked in public favour. Some dissenting voices were heard questioning the type of trees they planted, the quality of timber they produced, and the heavy annual sums they were costing the taxpayer, but this criticism had not yet had an effect on the outlook of their higher officials, who were said to adopt a lofty, slightly disdainful, and somewhat ruthless attitude towards opposition. For me to oppose them was for David again to take on Goliath in a type of combat which the Goliaths of this world usually win. For David to succeed, great care had to be taken over the site of the battle, and the pebbles from the brook had to be carefully chosen and the sling put in perfect working order; and even then he would have to look to Providence.

One day in October a Mr Moyers of the Forestry Commission came down. They wanted, he said, to demolish the Ashley Chase Woods because if they stopped work there, the department that had been formed to operate the new South Dorset Forest would have to be closed down, and the Ashley and Puncknowle woods would have to be given back.

I carefully deployed my arguments. Basing myself on Hutchins's *History of Dorset*, I explained that these woods of oak and ash must have been part of the original landscape in the time of the Druids, and have been there when the pre-Druidical temple up on Tenants Hill had been built. I took him up to Tenants Hill and showed him that a clear fell would create nothing but devastation, and that even if they left a thin screen of trees around the perimeter, it would not mitigate the effect because one could see right into the woods from the superior elevation of the surrounding hills. I then trotted out what I hoped would prove my trump card. I would be prepared to take the woods back and undertake to replant them, under their supervision if necessary, provided I could do it piecemeal, leaving sufficient cover, and plant only hardwoods. But what were these arguments in the face of bureaucratic empire-building? Moyers said that I had no rights in the matter, although I detected in his tone a preference for obtaining my agreement to a submission, if possible.

At the end of November he returned with Mr Penistone, the head forester of the Forestry Commission based in Bristol. I took him and Moyers with John Thacker and Reg Jones up to Tenants Hill, hoping to make the same effect on him as I thought I had made on Moyers; but by then the woods were leafless and shrouded in mist, and this time the sun was in our eyes. He did not seem impressed, and both Thacker and Jones fell silent, believing that there was nothing for it but to submit. I then led them all to the garden of Ashley Chase and showed him how from there a complete fell would be an act of sheer vandalism. Penistone said that in ten or fifteen years the woods would have been replanted, to which I replied that it was precisely the next ten or fifteen years that were most important to me. Once more I offered to buy the woods and replant under their supervision.

Suddenly Penistone turned round and mentioned that it might cost me £10,000, a sum far exceeding the market value. Then I discovered that, possibly at Moyer's instigation, they had brought with them an alternative plan. They would sell me the forty-five odd acres held under their lease to the east of the road, if they kept and were allowed to fell the fifty-five acres to the west of it. I accepted at once, though they qualified their agreement by saying that it would have to be approved by the Forestry Commission formally. Then there was silence until one day in May 1969 Reg Jones telephoned me to say that they had made an offer to return the forty-five acres east of the road for £1,350, the cost they had so far incurred in constructing the road in it, provided I also threw in for nothing a further fifteen acres of woodland west of the road but not leased to them, leaving them with seventy-seven acres all told.

Eventually all was agreed and set out in documents, and we received the unexpected but welcome support of one of the Forestry Commission's own men. It was part of the arrangement that there should be an 'amenity belt' surrounding the western woods, a belt of trees that would be left standing when the clear fell took place. He was a member of the Dorset Naturalists Association to whom I had several times given permission to wander at will through the woods. He helped to make the amenity belt quite wide so that the part left for the Forestry Commission to fell, which contained many steep slopes and much difficult terrain, was less than originally envisaged. It was my belief that the whole operation was quite uneconomic for the Forestry Commission.

Bureaucracy moves slowly and it was not until 1972 that we actually completed the contract to buy back the eastern woods. Nothing more happened until 1976, by which time the Forestry Commission had decided that it was time to make a clear fell of the western woods. Knowing that there was considerable local opposition, their Planning Committee decided to hold an inquiry at Ashley Dairy, for which purpose they sent two of their officials. So, I imagined, had Thomas Cromwell's officials appeared to the local monks and abbots when they had come down to value the monastery lands and sell them to the ravenous farmers, bailiffs, merchants and courtiers who gathered to bid. The meeting was held in the cowshed at the Dairy and was attended by representatives of the Council for the Preservation of Rural England, the Country Landowners Association and the West Dorset Planning Committee, as well as the Parish Councils of Litton and Puncknowle, all of whom I had aroused to take an interest in the woods.

We sat around on straw bales. The Commission officials said that the Planning Committee had no duty to hold this inquiry, nor any obligation to tell us what they intended to do, but, like the good chaps they were, they were volunteering the information. I interrupted to ask how much the clearing and road-making on this very difficult terrain, not to speak of the planting, maintenance and fencing, would cost in total, and per acre of planted woodland, and whether it was a viable undertaking in economic terms. The answer was that this was not our concern. I, however, considered it a perfectly proper public function to question the cost-effectiveness of a State-owned company.

They then produced a map of Long Wood and Chapel Wood, all of which they intended to have clear felled. I noticed that they had left a thin girdle of trees around the perimeter, but that it was not the map that had accompanied a letter they had sent me in 1972 at the exchange of contracts, in which they had set out the amenity belt they intended to leave when they came to fell the woods. I waved the letter of 1972 with the plan at them, and they appeared non-plussed, but everyone else was silent. Only the dairy cows in the neighbouring barn lowed and dunged, unwittingly giving what I regarded as this farce of a hearing a suitable response. And that was that.

They had held a meeting, explained what they intended to do, and now they were going to do it. Later that month the *Dorset Evening Echo* reported that the West Dorset Council wanted the Forestry Commission to surrender Ashley Woods, and the next day an article which I had drafted in conjunction with the local historian, John Bailey, appeared in the same newspaper. It was like so much water on a rhinoceros's back. Bridport Council then said that they too were opposed to the scheme. Another letter of mine appeared in the *Dorset Echo*, claiming that it would cost £800 an acre for the Forestry Commission to plant the thirty acres effectively permitted them by our agreement. Still nothing happened until one day the following Spring, when John Thacker announced that some bulldozers had appeared with instructions to start road-making in Long Coppice, preparatory to felling in the Autumn. I asked him which map they were using to delimit the amenity belt and ascertained that it was the new one, to which I had not agreed.

I immediately wrote to the Bristol headquarters of the Forestry Commission. Prior to this we had received some help from Jim Spicer, MP, and a somewhat mendacious letter from the Ministry of the Environment, one of those letters which while purporting to be fair and dispassionate, coolly omits the vital factors in the opponents' case. There had also been a further hearing in Litton Cheney which I had been unable to attend, and where the Forestry Commission had declined to produce the gentlemen's agreement with me which they had once said was as good as a contract. I now asked the Commission which plan they proposed to be guided by in their felling. The letter I received from the Conservator, Mr L.C. Troup, dated 7 March 1977, did not satisfy me. Mr Troup said that he saw no objection in principle to the procedure adopted at the meeting, which he claimed had resulted in total agreement. Dealing with the matter of the earlier undertaking between the Commission and myself for the retention of an amenity belt, had the matter rested there, he told me, he would have felt bound to honour the undertakings. However, matters had not rested there, since I had taken a leading part in involving local authorities and other bodies, including a Member of Parliament, so that the matter had been raised, as he put it, to a higher forum. He concluded by saying that the fresh proposals generated by the debate I had initiated replaced the original undertakings.

I replied on 23 March 1977, as follows:

I have your letter of 7 March and find its contents extraordinary. You appear to be telling me that because I took some part in calling public attention to the earlier plans your department had devised for the destruction of these woodlands, the Ministry of Agriculture is no longer bound by the contract it made with me on 22 December 1971.

Lest you should be in any further doubt of my position in the matter, may I make it clear that I have not released the Ministry from the agreement made with me on that date, which it considered binding on itself as well as me.

I now wish to know the intentions of the Forestry Commission. If their intentions are to proceed in violation of the agreement made with me, I will instruct my solicitors to act for me.

Again, nothing happened until in May 1978 John Thacker informed me that an employee of the Forestry Commission had informally mentioned that they intended to commence work on the Ashley Chase woodlands some time that year.

There was an uneasy truce until I received a letter from Mr Troup dated 6 July 1979 and written in a wholly different, and one might say contrite, manner. He told me that all government departments were engaged in financial reappraisals with the eminently worthy objective of getting rid of fat. The Forestry Commission had already halved their labour force and undertaken double the work by cost levels which, in real terms, had remained stable since about 1963. Part of the reappraisal included the role of small woodlands of the character of Ashley Chase. While he could not pre-empt the Minister's and Commissioners' decisions, it seemed to him not at all unlikely that the climate had changed to the degree that we should be able to pick up and dust down our abortive negotiations of a few years back, and words to that effect.

What had set off the earthquake that had caused this change of attitude? The Conservatives had won the Election of May 1979, and the Forestry Commission was one of those institutions upon which a sharp axe fell.

On 24 June 1980 I bought the remaining seventy-seven acres for £13,000. It was rather a high price but I was prepared to pay it to get the Commission completely off my land. It had taken fourteen years to do it, four years longer than it took the Greeks to capture Troy, but the battle was won and our valley saved.

CHAPTER *4*

Starting to Farm

I may hitherto have given the impression that this work to the house and garden and my preoccupation with preserving the woodlands had absorbed all the time I had available to give to Ashley Chase. But this was not so: I had come to farm and I immediately set about it. Russell Wood kept 800 ewes with their lambs on the estate, together with four or five house cows, and in addition had 100 beef cows 'on tack', which meant that other farmers were able to graze the summer grass for a shilling a day per head. I remember that when he had driven me over the fields in his Land Rover he had murmured, 'I would not run any more sheep here if I were you.' I should have taken his advice. I bought his 800 ewes, about 600 of their lambs and the house cows, but sent the cattle packing.

Within a month of our completing the purchase John Thacker had come to the conclusion that Russell Wood could not have been making money from the estate. That fortified me in disregarding his advice and buying in a further 600 ewes, of which 320 were Dorset Horns. These were said to have the inestimable advantage over other breeds of lambing whenever the shepherd liked, and therefore at Christmas, which enabled their lambs to be sold in time for the Easter trade, and thus to fetch £9 or £10 a head against the £6 or £7 a head for the Scots half-bred lambs that would not be ready till July. That was the theory. It sounded good and we soon had 1,500 ewes dotted about the hills and valleys and expected that by the following Spring and Summer we should have 2,300 lambs as well, a sight to cheer the heart of any flock master. At that time, I used to count sheep to get myself off to sleep. They were not sheep in the abstract but my own sheep and lambs, and the counting was connected with the sums likely to be brought in at the forthcoming lamb sales.

Counting sheep got me off to sleep, but the sheep did not justify my hopes in them, and for this there were several reasons. First of all, as Russell Wood had delicately hinted to us, the land was 'sheep-sick'. In other words, it had had too many sheep running around on it for too long. The result was that the pastures were full of little snail-like creatures that were ingested by the lambs as they nibbled the grass, causing them to have liver-fluke which in turn prevented them from putting on weight. The Dorset Horn lambs, which were supposed to be ready for market by April, failed therefore to make the requisite weight by then and had to be carried until August, when they were sold with the Scots half-bred lambs at £5 or £6 a head. Secondly, although we had two men doing shepherds' work, neither was really a trained shepherd, and anyone who tries to keep sheep in any numbers without the assistance of skilled shepherds is ill-advised.

Thirdly, while the books speak of keeping six or seven ewes per acre, they assume that lambing takes place in buildings or specially prepared fields, and that the flocks are moved from field to field pretty smartly. Fourthly, we lost many lambs through the depredations of foxes, and from crows and pigeons who would pick out the young lambs' eyes. Within a year or so we had realized that the sheep venture was bound to fail.

The question we then asked ourselves was what to do next.

Sunset over Golden Cap

The ha-ha and Ashley Chase house

The pavilion: 'In Xanadu did Kubla Khan a stately pleasure dome decree . . .'

From the four-volume set of Hutchins's *History of Dorset* which I dipped into from time to time, I discovered that there had been a dairy at Ashley in the sixteenth century on the site of the present sheep shed on Ashley Cow-leaze, just to the north of the western part of the woodlands. I reckoned that if a dairy could operate there four centuries ago, there was no good reason for not operating one there today, the soil and presumably the climate being much the same. I therefore began to look at the Ashley sheep shed as the site of a future dairy. The buildings there would have to be enlarged and additions made to them, and equipment would have to be installed. It would cost a bit, but the lure was the prospect of a steady monthly milk cheque.

Somewhat earlier, only two or three months after we had taken possession of Ashley Chase, John Thacker and I had sat in our garden and debated the direction our farming venture should take. He was not used to sheep and had perhaps a presentiment that an intensively stocked sheep ranch might not do too well. By this time we knew every field of the estate and could see the limitations of each. The south-east section of the estate, with fields bearing such names as Misery Mount, Near and Far Van Diemens, Quarry and Roughs, rather spoke for themselves in their names, which denoted remoteness, inaccessibility and an irregular surface. The whole picturesque area which lies just north of Wears Hill was a geological wonder. Perhaps, in ages gone by, the sea had slipped in under the Chesil Beach and caused a landslip, because the soil had an extraordinary variety in its horizontal dimension, with greensand, chalk, flint, clay and gravel jostling each other. There was neither water laid on nor road access, and no buildings whatsoever. Much the same could be said of the fields, called North and South Sands, to the south-west. The only land suitable for a dairy was about 130 acres in the vicinity of the Ashley sheep shed, and that would have to be a modest affair.

I then raised with John the possibility of acquiring additional land adjacent to us. It seemed unlikely that we should be lucky. Two years earlier, Francis Woodhouse, before he bought the nearby Puncknowle estate of 750 acres, had been offered Ashley Chase and had turned it down for the same considerations confronting us now: the rough uneven nature of the ground, and the unlikelihood of being able to extend it. We were hemmed in to the north and south by the Abbotsbury estate of the sixth Earl of Ilchester, who we considered was most unlikely to sell, and a narrow smallholding which led down the hill to Long Bredy; to the east by Gorwell Farm owned by the Pengelly family; and to the west by Parks Farm owned by Leslie Sorrell, who had once leased part of Ashley Chase. Nevertheless, on the principle of nothing ventured, nothing gained, I asked John to approach them all, which he did without much expectation of success.

To his surprise we learned by December that Leslie Sorrell would consider a sale, while the Ilchester estate was taking steps to recover vacant possession of Lower Kingston Russell Farm to the north of us from the tenant, Frank Hewer (who was a descendant of the originator of the Hereford breed of beef cattle). Reg Jones was instructed to negotiate for Parks Farm. By April 1967 talks had begun in earnest and by July terms had been agreed for the purchase. The price for its 180 acres was £42,000, which worked out at £230 an acre. I also bought the eighty head of cattle it carried. (Sorrell used the money to buy a bigger farm down the valley at Shipton Gorge). This purchase added to Ashley Chase a narrow but fertile strip of land running from the South Sands down to the fertile alluvial soil of the lower levels of the Bride Valley, and gave us a ready-made if old-fashioned four-a-side breast-high milking parlour with rudimentary buildings to shelter cattle and store hay. It increased our overall acreage to 860 and increased the proportion of usable land to unproductive woodland considerably. By November we were obtaining 200 gallons of milk daily from the herd, which we were hoping to increase to eighty-five cows.

A curious coincidence was revealed when, some time in October 1967, I found myself perusing the title deeds of Parks Farm. I happened at the same time to be reading the *Chronicles of Holland House* by the sixth Earl of Ilchester, who coincidentally was also the freeholder of my London house, when I came upon this passage about Mrs Norton, Lord Melbourne's mistress:

> Mrs Norton's youngest sister married Lord Seymour, Duke of Somerset. Their brother, Brinsley, distinguished himself in 1835 by eloping with Marcia Grant, the daughter of Sir Colquhoun Grant, and heiress to Frampton Court.

And there in front of me lay some indentures of 1886 and 1888 recording the names of Sir Colquhoun Grant, Marcia Grant and Richard Brinsley Sheridan, the grandson of the playwright, all of Frampton Court.

An auction of Lower Kingston Russell Farm, with vacant possession, was eventually announced for 18 September, in the Oak Room of 'The Antelope' in Dorchester, the very room in which Judge Jeffreys had sat to try Dorset men for treason in the wake of Monmouth's rebellion in those trials which evoked the term 'Bloody Assizes'.

On auction day, Richard Thorpe and Reg Jones lunched with Colette and me at Ashley to discuss the limits to which we should go. I resolved to pay up to £111,000 or £326 an acre, but hoped that the farm would be knocked down to me for £95,000 or £280 an acre. In a mood of some excitement we left for Dorchester.

John Thacker, Frank Hewer and Michael Pengelly were among a sprinkling of others in a half-empty room. The auction began, with Reg Jones bidding for me. The bidding appeared to falter at £88,000, then recovered to £95,000 where it seemed to stop, until a new voice took it up, bidding, I learned much later, for Francis Woodhouse of the neighbouring Puncknowle estate. He dropped out at £103,000, at which price the property was knocked down to me. As John drove me back to Ashley in the Land Rover that evening, he said, 'Your name will be on a lot of tongues down the valley tonight.' No doubt it was.

This farm of 340 acres had belonged to the Dukes of Bedford, and drew attention to the first Earl of Bedford, who had been born lower down the valley at Berwick Farm. It had been bought by the Ilchester Trustees but as it was not contiguous with the rest of their estate, they had now determined to sell it to provide capital for improving their home farm. It was a solid block of land a mile long from north to south and half a mile wide from east to west. Its northern boundary for the most part was formed by the River Bride; and the water meadows adjacent thereto, comprising silt washed down from Tenants Hill, constituted some of the richest soil in the Bride Valley. Then it ran south up Tenants Hill, over its crest and down a little to link up with us. The soil was somewhat thinner on top of the hill where a six-inch layer of loam lay on chalk and flint, but it was all good for grazing, silaging, haymaking and corn growing, save for the steep escarpment leading up to the flat crest of the 630-foot hill. Here lay the well-known Kingston Russell Stone Circle, an arrangement of monolithic stones, fallen some time ago, and dating from about 1800 BC in the pre-Celtic era . Near it lay a former hut circle and an oval enclosure of the later Bronze Age. Nearby these ancient relics, and forming part of the boundary between the farm and the Williams's

Bridehead estate, was a mysterious-looking and splendid beech grove, the home of numbers of rookeries, and possibly the successor of the sacred grove which sheltered the priests of this ancient temple complex.

The views from the crest of the hill were breathtaking. The whole of the Bride Valley lay below it, and beyond to the west one could see as far as the flashing windows of Lyme Regis, sixteen miles away, the heights of Pilsdon and Lewesdon, and beyond them to the uplands of Dartmoor. As the birds soared and glided over the valley, it took little imagination to envisage the past and to wonder if the valley of the Bride had, from that height, looked very different to the Romano-Britons or their predecessors. It was just as well that the vendors of this farm had not known that its beauty and the magnificent vistas it possessed over land and sea had played quite a part in determining me to be in the auction hall that afternoon.

So, within twenty-two months of taking possession of Ashley Chase, I had extended its area from 680 acres to 1,200 acres. As Richard Thorpe had said, I was moving into the realms of the big farmer. I was certainly now the owner of the largest farm in hand in the Bride Valley. I had been bitten by the farming bug quite deeply, and a great change in my circumstances now took place. Until the purchase of Lower Kingston Russell Farm, I had used my own money. Now I began to borrow. I rather think that, when they saw me plunge into purchase after purchase, the farmers of the Bride Valley thought that I had a bottomless treasure chest to which I could have recourse whenever a new farm appeared on the market. I wish it had been so, for then I would have been spared the anxieties associated with rising interest rates and borrowing restrictions. In fact the development of the Ashley Chase estate was largely effected on borrowed

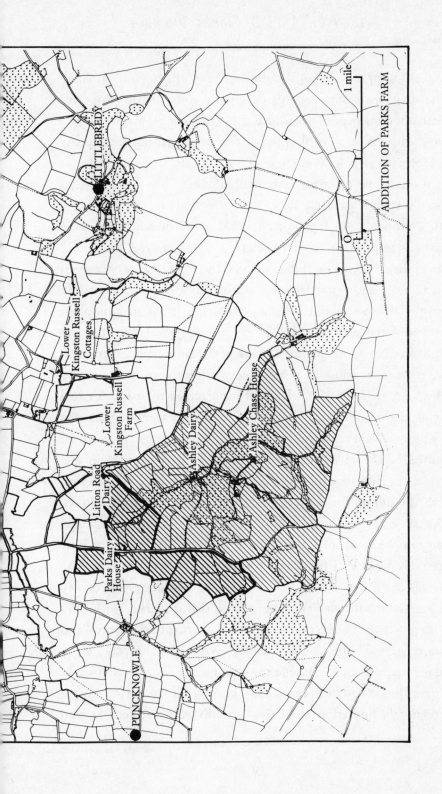

LITTLEBREDY

Lower Kingston Russell Cottages

Lower Kingston Russell Farm

Litton Road Dairy

Ashley Dairy

Ashley Chase House

Parks Dairy House

PUNCKNOWLE

1 mile

ADDITION OF PARKS FARM

money, although every now and then I was able to clear off some of the debt with the proceeds of sale of some urban property. Eventually my finances resembled those of a conglomerate organization where a successful enterprise in one field bolsters up the development of a new enterprise in a totally different field. It turned out to be a source of overall stability, but I confess that along the road it gave me more than a few anxious moments.

By October 1968 I possessed 1,200 acres of land that were singularly unproductive. They held a few hundred sheep and about eighty dairy cows at Parks Farm. Much of Dorset was given over to dog and stick farming at that time, so the inactivity presented by the enlarged Ashley Chase estate at that moment would not have been considered as all that untypical, but I had not bought all these farms merely to look at the landscape. I wanted to make them as productive as possible, within the proved capacity of the land, regardless of what had occurred in the past. We had convinced ourselves that the soil and climate were suitable for dairying, and there were dairies (of no great size, it must be admitted) in the valley that seemed to do well. The problem was to create the infrastructure which could support intensive dairying and then build up the herds whose milk would justify the outlay.

Dorset is probably the most beautiful and most unspoiled county in the south of England. It was then also one of the least intensively farmed. I think there were two reasons for this. The first was the absence of industrial cities or seaside resorts of any real size, which meant that there was no major market for locally grown produce. The second was the hilly nature of the central and western part of the county which, with its relatively heavy rainfall, made it more suitable for grazing than for arable use. In the past Dorset had been principally known for its sheep. Only in the relatively limited areas of river meadows had it been known for its dairies. Roads were winding and narrow, where they existed at all, and communications, except to and from the principal towns, were consequently slow. Modern farming methods seemed to stop at Hampshire. As owner of a large tract of downs and coombes which had hardly been farmed seriously at all, I was facing a considerable challenge.

Early in 1969 John Foot, the principal farmer in Long Bredy, indicated that he was prepared to sell a strip of land seventy acres in extent, adjacent to the western boundary of Lower Kingston Russell Farm. By September its purchase had been completed for £355 an acre, and we now had a solid self-contained farming unit at Lower Kingston Russell bordering on Abbotsbury Lane and totalling 410 acres. That farm had once supported a 100-cow herd. We thought that, enlarged and modernized, it could now support a 220-cow dairy. Parks had once supported an eighty-cow dairy, which we thought could be increased to 100 cows, and while Ashley itself had not in modern times had a dairy at all, a further 100-cow dairy could be installed there. Finally, with the acquisition of Parks Farm with its rich pastures, we decided to build a new 220-cow dairy on a virgin site near Dantze Coppice. The target, then, was to build up four dairies, comprising 640 dairy cows, virtually from scratch.

Before we started we had to take an important policy decision regarding the nature of the Winter feed we should provide for the cattle. The herds in the Bride Valley, and in most of Dorset, relied on hay, the traditional Winter food. It had its merits. It could be highly nutritious if of good quality. It could be easily stored in open Dutch barns and in the fields under the familiar tarpaulin-covered haystacks. It was, however, very dependent on the weather. A good dry Summer could supply a splendid crop, but should the Summer prove wet or the sea mist blow in, the

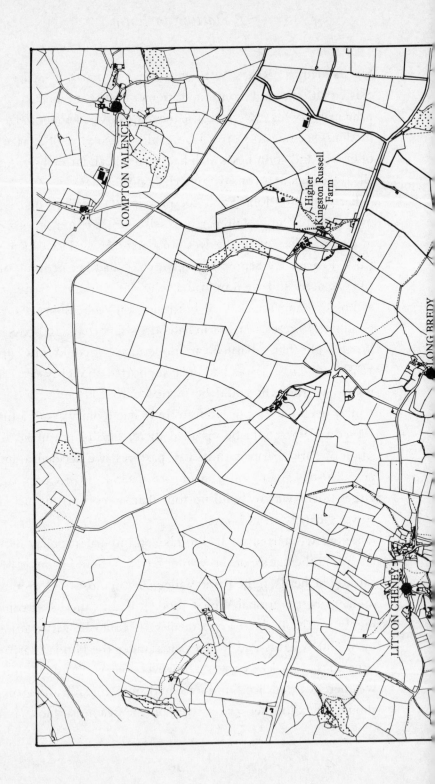

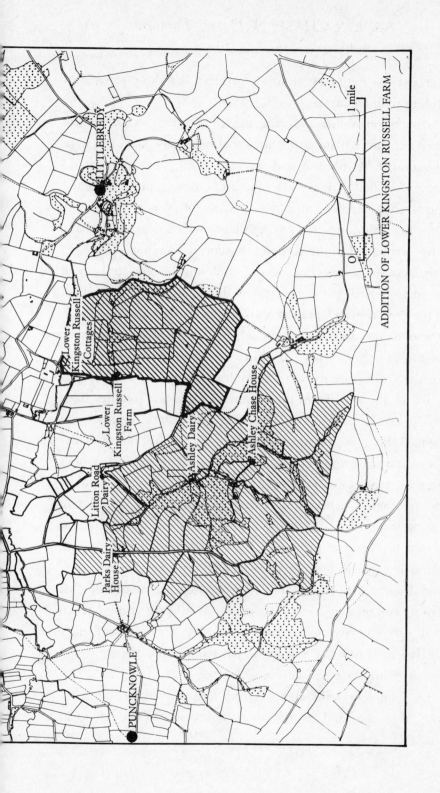

LITTLEBREDY

Lower
Kingston Russell
Cottages

Lower
Kingston Russell
Farm

Litton Road
Dairy

Ashley Dairy

Parks Dairy
House

Ashley Chase House

PUNCKNOWLE

O

1 mile

ADDITION OF LOWER KINGSTON RUSSELL FARM

resultant crops might be almost worthless, let alone capable of providing maintenance and milk.

A second possibility was the use of dried grass. This also entailed expensive plant and a huge fuel bill. I saw such a system working near Wimborne and rejected it, for not only could valuable time be lost if the machine broke down, but its product seemed only a supplement to hay or silage anyway.

The third solution was to make silage, which is green herbage that has fermented in the complete absence of oxygen. There are various systems but the best is to cut and wilt the crop in the field before it is ensiled, then harvest it with forage harvesters, which pick up the crop and pour it into tractor-hauled trailers which transport it into a covered barn where it is piled up with buck rakes and pressed down by tractors, then covered with molasses or formic acid before having a tarpaulin laid over it. The silage is then fed to the herd from the Autumn, when the pastures have given up, until the new grass is ready in the Spring. Or rather, the cattle feed themselves with it as and when they feel like it. It has the benefit of ensuring that the farmer is left with adequate stocks of preserved grass for six to seven months in the year, regardless of the weather. Quality could vary, much depended on it being cut at the right time, and being properly ensiled, but it could at least be relied upon to provide a cow's maintenance, and if good, could yield a gallon of milk a day as well without concentrate.

The drawback of the method was the expense involved. One had to reckon on a cow eating seven tons of silage a year, so that a herd of 640 cows would need something like 4,480 tons of silage annually, besides what would be needed for the young stock. Permanent buildings, usually constructed with steel-framed re-inforced concrete walls and concrete floors, were required for storing the grass, and the buildings had to be tall enough to be filled with grass up to a height of seven to eight feet from the ground, plus the height of the tractor that was used to fill it up and bank it down. This was in addition to the cubicled cowsheds, built with the same materials, needed to house the herds. Then expensive equipment was needed to cut the silage, harvest it, transport it and pack it in, not to speak of a team to man the equipment. If the investment was made, it bought security; and for us, being so near the coast, situated in the West Country with its unpredictable Summers, and contemplating the holding of so many cattle, there was, in my view, no real alternative.

In the 1930s it would have taken the labour of two men and a boy to milk about forty cows twice daily. By the 1950s improvements in the design of milking parlours enabled one man to milk sixty cows. With the design of the herring-bone parlour, the cubicled cattle-house and the self-feed silage barn, one man could be made responsible for 120 cows, especially since it was unlikely that all those cows would be yielding milk at the same time. We therefore formulated plans, wherever we could, to build dairies of 100 to 120 cows to be tended by one dairyman and dairies of 200 to 240 cows to be tended by two men, the size depending on the available grazing area around the dairy.

In those days planning committees were the bane of our lives. If one wanted to qualify for a 30 per cent or, in some years, a 40 per cent grant on new farm buildings, one had to draw up plans beforehand that required planning permission from the local office of the Ministry of Agriculture which, for us, was in Dorchester, before the Ministry would give a certificate that the dairy would be grant-aided. This planning permission commonly took four months to obtain, or even longer if there was any disagreement, even on a small issue, between one's building surveyor and the Ministry. Therefore, if we drew up our plans in the Winter to erect a new dairy before the end of the Summer, when outdoor conditions were supposedly ideal for building, it invariably happened that because of planning delays, we would only be able to start by the Summer, and inevitably finished amid the quagmires caused by the Autumn rains. However, if one wanted to take the benefit of the grant, one had to put up with the vagaries of the system.

The decisions of planning committees could be quirky indeed, as we experienced at Lower Kingston Russell. I wanted a 220-cow two-man dairy there, and we planned for two cow-houses, capable of holding 120 cows each, to be erected just north of the existing cow-house which, we thought, could be converted to a silage barn. Planning permission for the scheme was refused for no obvious good reason. So we came up with an alternative scheme that won approval, which was for one cow-house north of the existing buildings, and another up the hill, above the farmhouse and to the south of it. It would have been more to the point had we talked to old Mr Foster Symes who then lived on a spur of Whatcombe Hill opposite, for he had farmed Lower Kingston Russell as a tenant of both the Duke of Bedford and the Earl of Ilchester for years, prior to his retirement, and could have told us what would happen.

One day in February 1970 I took a walk with Cedric, my younger son, to Lower Kingston Russell Farm, to see how work was progressing. We saw two bulldozers digging into the hillside and I took photographs to compare the scene with what I hoped would be erected in two or three months' time. After lunch I went back with Roby, my elder son. Work had stopped, one of the bulldozers had sunk five feet into the ground, and water was pouring out of the hillside. I immediately telephoned Eddie Fry, and the next day we met to discuss the situation. We knew that the farm drew its water from springs on the north side of Tenants Hill, but not that the area surrounding the outlet was a great sponge. The planners had in fact directed us to build a large dairy complex on top of a bog! A year's planning went for a 'Burton', but we had fortunately avoided a much worse disaster. Had we built in the Summer, the sub-soil would have been dry enough to support the dairy buildings . . . until the Autumn when, with the seasonal rains, the water levels would have risen, and the buildings would have collapsed.

So we went back to a variation of an earlier scheme for two eighty-cow cubicled cow-houses with a herringbone parlour in between them. Planning permission was given in April, and a useful price review at that moment meant that I should get a 40 per cent grant instead of the 30 per cent for the abortive scheme. It was a case of 'All's Well That Ends Well', but the episode illustrates how the planners and the Ministry men who doled out grants could breezily delay, divert or abort a well-considered plan for expansion. Years later we would build a third cubicled cow-house for eighty cows and a further silage barn to enable Lower Kingston Russell Dairy to carry 240 cows.

In the midst of this development we heard that Colonel Christopher (Robin) Wordsworth wanted to sell his 330-acre Baglake Farm, which lay between Parks Farm and the village of Litton Cheney. It had a seventeenth-cum-eighteenth-century manor house with a walled garden, and Robin had farmed it since the 1930s. When he retired from the Army at the end of the war, his 100 Ayrshire dairy herd had, for a time, been the largest in the Bride Valley. Owing to personal reasons, he had to sell his farm, although he was obviously reluctant to do so. His land stretched for one and a half miles from the border of Parks up the south face of Whatcombe Down on the A35 road. I was offered it for

£120,000, or £360 an acre, though much of the land which lay between the house and the 700-foot crest of Whatcombe Hill was fairly rough. I did not relish the cost of keeping up a 300-year-old manor house in which I did not propose to live, nor did I like the idea of being the means, however innocent, of bringing to an end the Colonel's forty-year farming career in the Bride Valley. Instead, I made an offer for those fields of Baglake, amounting to 140 acres, which lay between Litton Cheney and Parks Farm. These, were we to secure them, would enable us to round out the estate on its north-west boundaries, give us some water meadows on the Bride, and a block of very fertile land, just south of the village, called 'The Mount'. A successful negotiation would give us the necessary land to build a new 220-cow dairy at Parks, just below Dantze Coppice.

Robin Wordsworth went to consult his old friend, Lionel King, the former owner of the Puncknowle estate, who convinced him that he could milk his 100-cow herd on half his existing acreage, and who also told him of rumours he had heard of my being interested in Cruxton Manor Farm, and that he had better strike while the iron was hot. The first piece of advice proved correct, but the rumour was ill-founded. Together they prompted Robin to sell me 140 acres with two small cottages on them for £42,000, a sale that was completed by November 1970.

I had therefore, by 1970, either built or set myself to build four dairies for 640 dairy cows. All this building and planning required a considerable programme for providing ancillary services. The first requirement was water. Lower Kingston Russell Dairy functioned on spring water, of which there was adequate supply. Ashley Chase house, and the four cottages that went with it, drew their water from the river and it was virtually undrinkable. The fields to the south, east and west of Ashley Chase house had no

The Shooting Box cottage

Parks Farm and the cheese dairy in the Bride Valley

John Thacker with a friendly goat

Ian Thacker with his calves

water supply at all. Only Parks had its own water supply.

The nearest mains water was at Litton Cheney, two miles to the north of our house and at least a mile from Parks and the site of the Litton Dairy. It gushed out from abundant springs on the slopes of Whatcombe Down just north of the village, whence it was piped by the Water Board to the village of Puncknowle via Looke Farm. When I purchased Parks Farm, my western boundary was only 200 to 300 yards from the main pipe at Looke. One day John Thacker went to see eighty-year-old Mr Pike at Looke Manor. The old gentleman was seated at his fireside with a whisky bottle in his hand; John was not quite certain what his reaction would be to a proposal to connect a feeder pipe from the mains on his land and run it into Ashley Chase. By the time they had finished the bottle of whisky, everything had been agreed. We would, at my expense, lay a mole-pipe about four feet underground from the junction on Looke Farm to Ashley Chase house, its cottages and its various water-troughs. We would run it under the woodland ride cleared by the Forestry Commission for the greater part of the one and a half miles to the Ashley Chase reservoir, whence it would run by gravity to the house and its cottages. It cost me £1,500 but transformed living conditions for those who lived in the cottages, made dairying possible at Ashley and Litton, and enabled us to move into our house.

The next step was to build roads. Apart from the macadamized road from Abbotsbury to Ashley, which urgently required resurfacing, there were no surfaced roads on the estate. There were two dirt tracks, which were mud-tracks in Winter impassable to motorcars and lorries, and hardly less so in Summer because of the deep ruts left by tractors. Without decent roads, it was impossible to open dairies with the concomitant need for milk-lorries, cattle-feed lorries, and other trade suppliers and

COMPTON VALENCE

Higher
Kingston Russell
Farm

LONG BREDY

LITTON CHENEY

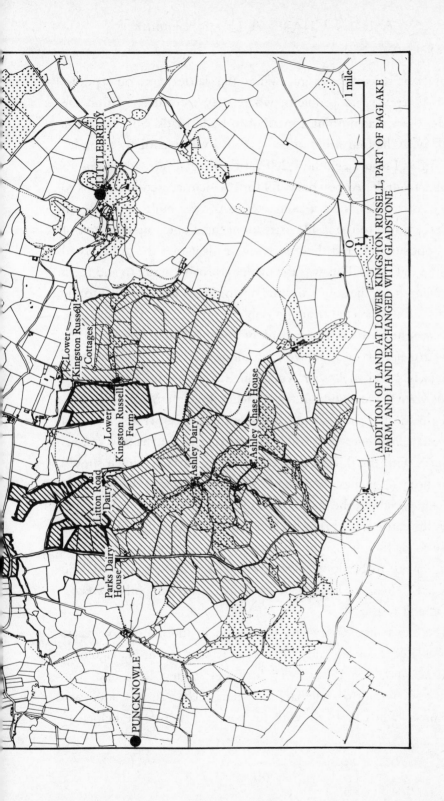

LITTLEBREDY

Lower
Kingston Russell
Cottages

Lower
Kingston Russell
Farm

Litton Road
Dairy

Ashley Dairy

Ashley Chase House

Parks Dairy
House

PUNCKNOWLE

0   1 mile

ADDITION OF LAND AT LOWER KINGSTON RUSSELL, PART OF BAGLAKE
FARM, AND LAND EXCHANGED WITH GLADSTONE

technicians to come and go. Where the dairies were on a public road, there was no problem; where they were deep within the estate, there was nothing for it but to build roads. So a start was made with the four miles or so of roads I was eventually to build. First of all I resurfaced the 1,200 yards of metalled road leading to Ashley from the Abbotsbury hill fort, which secured our access to the coast road. Then a concrete road was built from Beech Cottage down to the Ashley stream in the woods, up the flank of the opposite hill, and then north-west till it met the public road leading to Litton. This was the main axis road leading to and from the estate from the south and the north. Spurs branched off to the new beef unit erected near the Ashley cottages, to Ashley Dairy, and straight up the southern flank of Tenants Hill to link up with a 250-yard hard-core road we built along its crest to Abbotsbury Lane which led to Lower Kingston Russell Farm. The concrete roads were ten feet wide and four inches thick on top of hard-core, and constituted the first north-to-south all-weather road system the estate had ever possessed. In retrospect, we made a serious mistake with the thickness of the concrete surface, which should have been six inches. We simply had not visualized the increased size and weight of the lorries and tankers that would one day come with the cattle feed, bring the fuel and take our milk. The cost of these roads then was approximately £1 a square yard. Then there was fencing to be done, defective drainage to be remedied, and neglected fields to be cleared of couch grass and other weeds, limed and fertilized.

This constant activity and expansion in those first five years necessitated a considerable increase in labour and in management control, and here I was very lucky in having John and Joan Thacker's family to fall back on. Ian, their younger son, was seventeen when he came with his parents. At first he helped to clear the garden, work he, as a born cattleman, did not enjoy. Then he took charge of the sheep, dipping them, worming them, shearing them and, where necessary, assisting them to lamb, but, not being a trained shepherd, I do not think he was too happy with that work either. His hour came when we turned to dairying, and kept 200 heifers and young steers in our heifer and beef enterprises. He had been trained by his father to manage cattle. That was what he loved doing, and by 1968 that was what he was doing. He was placed in overall charge, under his father, of all the dairies and other cattle enterprises, and by taking over relief milking acquired a first-hand knowledge of every dairy cow as well as beef animal on the estate. He had an older brother, David, then about twenty years of age, who had stayed in Guildford to court his future wife. They were a close family and David soon expressed a wish to join his parents; with Valerie secured, he came to Ashley in 1967. He was an expert tractor driver, could manipulate tractors and trailers in the worst conditions, and would go out, like Ian, in all weather and in every emergency. He was placed in charge of all field work. The chain of command was soon in competent hands.

Another thing that occurred in this early period was a kind of 'musical chairs' over houses. At first John and Joan lived with Ian and two of their girls, Jane and Wendy, in Shooting Box, some 220 yards from the 'big house'. Joan liked the roomy cottage and before long had named Ashley Chase 'Happy Valley', which aptly expressed the tranquillity of the woods and meadows around the big house, of which she also took care. But once Lower Kingston Russell, with its big farmhouse and two cottages, was acquired, off she moved with her family there, leaving David and Valerie ensconced in Shooting Box.

By the end of 1971, which marked five and a half years from the time we took possession of Ashley Chase, we had extended the estate from 680 to 1,410 acres and built up the dairy herd from nothing to 367 dairy cows with 223 followers, distributed over three dairies.

CHAPTER 5

Farming and Politics

I took up farming without knowing the slightest thing about it. But within five years I had achieved a certain knowledge of the subject by dint of reading various books on dairying, grass conservation, animal nutrition, animal diseases, slurry disposal, road building and the history of farming. I learned still more through John Thacker and through the actual process of practical farming. I had, through these various sources, accumulated a certain knowledge and acquired a 'feel' for agriculture.

I saw that a nation's agriculture had to be viewed in the context of its history, climate, soil, population and state of economic development. British agriculture had been, by and large, very prosperous throughout most of the eighteenth century and for most of the first seventy years of the nineteenth century. A growing population had ensured continual and rising demand. The wars with France had from time to time kept out imports. Improvements made by progressively-minded landowners and farmers, aided by agronomists, had, through the enclosure of common lands, improved drainage and hedging; and the introduction of new crops, the rotation of crops, improved animal husbandry and better farm implements had all ensured rising production.

But the continuous industrialization of Britain, which went

hand in hand with a rising population that virtually quadrupled during the course of the nineteenth century, led politicians and farmers to look for additional sources of supply. From the 1790s Britain was no longer self-sufficient in grain. The remedy at first lay in importing from Russia and Poland. Later, people looked to the vast new territories being opened up to grazing and arable farming in North and South America, and then in Australia and New Zealand.

The great new cornlands and pastures of the American Mid-West first enticed men and capital. Coincident with the development of the steamship and the railway, great new territories south of the Great Lakes were opened up to agriculture, and the grain and beef grown were conveyed by a railway and shipping network centred on Chicago which enabled the produce of those lands to be imported into Britain in great volume, and cheaper than they could be produced at home. It was the prospect of this inundation of foreign grain and meat which attracted the supporters of the repeal of the Corn Laws and the doctrine of Free Trade, and repelled their opponents. Although repeal of the Corn Laws was conceded in principle by Sir Robert Peel in 1848, the effects feared by British agricultural interests were slower in coming than had been expected. It was not until the 1870s that the network of railways and shipping centred on the Great Lakes allowed for a great importation of American food into Britain. It then coincided with a massive urbanization of the British population, resulting in a preponderance of the manufacturing over the agricultural interest.

Politicians, particularly Liberal politicians, saw the British economy as being predominantly based on becoming and remaining the workshop of the world. To maintain effective competition, particularly when much of the raw material required by the manufacturers needed to be imported, wages had to be kept low, and captive markets, or markets where Britain enjoyed preferential terms, had to be found and retained. It was thought that if food could be supplied cheaply for the manufacturing population, wages could be restrained, and a great edge over other manufacturing countries, which had no similar resource open to them, be obtained. Moreover, if the new overseas nations, with their agriculturally-based economies, could be led by tariff agreements, and by the simple process, dictated by self-interest, of buying manufactured goods from the principal buyer of their agricultural produce, a solid and enduring trading pattern would be created on which a strong and thriving British industry would be based.

This was, however, paid for by the collapse of British agriculture. A phenomenal fall in the value of agricultural land in the 1880s followed a fall in the price of agricultural produce, agricultural wages, agricultural investment and agricultural production. This, in turn, expedited a flight from the land, which produced the labour that the expanding industries in the new industrial cities required, and reinforced the growing urban bias of the population as a whole.

One unforeseen effect of this policy was to emerge in the course of the two World Wars. It was that Britain, having become so dependent on overseas-grown food, tempted any enemy with a powerful fleet to entertain the idea of starving the country into surrender; a great part of the British war effort was simply devoted to keeping the country fed through the provision and protection of Atlantic food convoys.

Another unforeseen effect was to occur in the industries so painstakingly fostered. Without the chill air of competition, manufacturers had little inducement to be efficient or innovative. The relative decline in British industry, which has become so pronounced in this century, started in the last third of the nineteenth century. It owed a good deal to the attitudes inculcated by reliance on safe, captive markets created by the tariffs set up under a system of Imperial preference and its fore-runners, whereby cheap overseas food and raw materials were imported in exchange for cheap manufactured goods. This policy encouraged British manufacturers to believe that it was unnecessary to search out new markets, install modern equipment, shed unnecessary labour and invent new products.

A good illustration of how far the collapse of farming prosperity proceeded in the period from 1880 to 1940 may be given by comparing the average value of agricultural land in 1938, which was about £10 per acre, with good land at the time of the Napoleonic wars, when it could fetch £50 an acre, remembering that the value of money in the 1930s was perhaps only a fifth of what it was in 1810. The closeness of Britain to defeat in the Second World War as a result of submarine warfare made the politicians take a more realistic view of the importance of British agriculture to the nation, and a serious attempt was made to rescue British farming from the state of dereliction into which it had fallen.

A great deal was done, comparatively speaking, to encourage production, modernize farm buildings, improve drainage and encourage the use of better farm equipment, while improved breeding methods and seeds led to greater yields in grass, corn and milk. The method used was one which relied on government grants for various schemes of improvement and carefully controlled prices for each commodity. This permitted progress in farming techniques without big profits being made by farmers, or good wages being paid to farm workers, whose salaries were still no more than a third or half those that could earned with comparable skills in industry.

Farming and Politics

A shrinking agricultural population meant less political influence for the agricultural community as a whole. The consumer commanded far more votes than this particular sector of producers, and as the consumer continued to want cheap food, the agricultural producer was given just enough encouragement to increase production by a stick and carrot policy that forced him to do so if he wished to avoid bankruptcy.

However, by the early 1960s, it was possible to envisage radical changes. First of all, new factors were influencing the prospects for cheap food. A growth in population in the great food-producing countries, coupled with the emergence of other food-importing nations, heralded the end of Britain's privileged position as the sole major food importer, able in consequence to impose prices and trade policies on its suppliers.

A second and more pressing challenge to its cheap food policy was the existence of the Common Market. The impetus towards a union of western European countries had been given by Churchill himself soon after the end of the Second World War. It had two main aims, the final liquidation of that political rivalry between France and Germany which had torn the fabric of European civilization to shreds three times in less than a century; and the abolition of national barriers to trade, which could lead to the creation of a trading bloc equal in size to that formed by the United States, and the creation of an economy which would provide for its inhabitants a similar per capita wealth.

It was ironic that after the impetus given by Churchill to the formation of a Common Market of western European nations to which Britain would belong, successive British governments should then have done their best to stifle its birth and, when that failed, attempt its destruction. The Foreign Office can be blamed for this policy, and it forms one of a long line of historic blunders which collectively succeeded in reducing Britain from a great Imperial power to a nation in the second or third rank, in a singularly short span of time. Its policy may have been guided by old-fashioned views of the importance of maintaining the former balance of power in western Europe, and by a misplaced belief that Britain's special relationship with the United States would be prejudiced by joining an economic union that might eventually be seen by America as a powerful trade rival.

When Labour governments were in power, a further argument against joining was the fact that membership of an economic union dedicated to the principle of free, unhindered and fair trade between its members was incompatible with a Socialist system that depended on subsidized industries, producer cartels, state monopolies and rigged trading conditions.

But anyone who could see a little into the future could foresee that the moment the Common Market felt strong enough to erect a high tariff against imports, Britain, if it continued to keep outside, would be in an exposed and dangerous position. Against a trading community of 180,000,000 people, what could a nation of 55,000,000 people on its borders do, particularly if it depended on international trade for its existence? The alternatives to joining eventually were either impossible or unattractive. Britain could conceivably apply to join the United States and effectively become a part of that country. It could conceivably join the Russian trading bloc, and ensure a catastrophic decline in its living standards and, likewise, a loss of its independence. It could consider an economic union with its overseas Dominions and former Colonies, but these markets collectively were limited and would not compensate for those that would be closed to Britain by tariff barriers, and it presumed a desire, which did not exist, on the part of those Dominions and Colonies for such a trading bloc.

The last alternative was to build a rival European commercial union based on those countries that were still outside the Common Market and with economies which depended to a considerable extent on exporting food to Britain, or which, because they too were Socialistic, had their own fears of belonging to a large and powerful free-market trading union. Thus the ramshackle EFTA group of trading countries, comprising Austria, Britain, Denmark, Eire, Iceland and Norway, came into existence. It always looked a temporary affair which would collapse whenever Britain changed its policy and joined the Common Market, to which it was never a serious rival or alternative.

By the 1960s the British government of Harold Macmillan had come to the conclusion that, having failed to destroy the Common Market or achieve any worthwhile alternative, nothing remained but to apply to join it. A great obstacle was then discovered in the determination of General de Gaulle to ensure that we would not be allowed in. He suspected that, having failed to topple it from without, Britain, should it be admitted, might well wish to undermine it from within, and would always work towards an Anglo-American trading and power bloc as opposed to a Continental one.

To a careful observer it was obvious that one day, sooner or later, Britain would join the Common Market. It would, no doubt, have to wait until de Gaulle relinquished power. It would also have to wait until a Conservative government came to office again, for the left wing of the Labour Party would never permit its leaders to initiate serious negotiations to that end. The Conservative Party had every inducement to join the Common Market, and its members, save for a relatively small percentage who imagined that Britain was still an Imperial power and that a British

Empire trading bloc was still a feasible alternative, realized that were we to remain out of it, the terms of trade would run more and more against us, our manufacturers would be increasingly shut out of overseas markets and the price of food would soar without compensatory advantages. They also knew that membership of a free-market economic union would be the most effective way to prevent the growing socialization of the economy and would eventually lead to the dismantling of existing socialist institutions. The Liberal Party supported membership for much the same reasons.

So Labour politicians and Trade Union leaders could rant as much as they liked against Britain joining the Common Market, and de Gaulle could refuse us entry as often as we applied; for when he relinquished power, the moment we had a non-Socialist government, the opportunity would be taken to apply for membership. Of course, when that moment came we would have to accept the terms offered to us. Had we joined with France, Germany and Italy, our ministers could have marched to the negotiating table with heads held high and imposed their own terms. We now came in as relative beggars joining a rich men's club with long established rules. We were made to crawl and had to accept the rules as they were, and were even then pathetically joyful when we were admitted. It was the price Britain paid for the short-sighted stupidity of its post-war governments.

But what might be distasteful to Trade Union leaders, the Foreign Office and some British politicians might be very acceptable to British farmers. They would, in effect, be changing masters. Instead of the politicians and bureaucrats of Whitehall, they would get the bureaucrats and politicians in Brussels. There was nothing necessarily wrong with that if one looked at it from the farmers' point of view, since it meant exchanging the rule of an urban-based electorate with a negligible farming constituent, which had oppressed the farming population for the best part of a century, for another body which treated farmers as well as any other industrial or commercial interest.

It therefore behoved anyone with a large stake in farming to try to assess the effect on British agriculture of Britain's eventual accession to the Common Market. The latter included countries possessing large agricultural populations with strong political influence. In some of them, up to one quarter of the working population worked on the land, as opposed to 3 per cent in Britain. Moreover, France and Holland were not merely self-sufficient in many foodstuffs but were great exporters of agricultural produce. Neither they nor the other Common Market countries had ever been submitted to a cheap-food policy based on imported food and resulting in an impoverished and abandoned countryside, and they had no intention of submitting to one to please Britain. In fact, apart from Iron and Steel, Agriculture was the one field where a united Common Market policy had been worked out in detail, and it was obvious that they had no intention of amending it to suit Britain's imagined interests. It therefore seemed sensible to look forward to a state of affairs when the condition of British agriculture would approximate to that obtaining in the Common Market countries. That could be easily observed, and it seemed that the British farmer could look forward eventually to a tripling in value of many agricultural products, a tripling of wages, of building costs and other inputs, and as a result, the tripling in value of agricultural land. Agriculture would, in fact, cease to be the Cinderella of the British economy, and be given the favoured conditions granted other segments of the economy.

I came to these conclusions in about 1967 or 1968. I could have been quite wrong. We could, for instance, have quietly slid into the position of a Socialist Soviet state, in which case I would have felt a misguided fool, but I thought that if rational counsels prevailed, things would go roughly as I had foreseen.

In the given and imagined circumstances, what then should I as a dairy farmer do? Taking into account that Britain then produced only 15 per cent of its own butter, 38 per cent of its own cheese, 100 per cent of its own milk and 80 per cent of its own meat, and that one aim of the Common Market was to make itself self-sufficient in food production insofar as the climate of its constituents permitted, the sensible thing seemed to be to produce as much of these products as I could. The supporters of entry into the Common Market maintained that each region within it would be free to produce what it did best. It was clear that there were few regions, if any, in western Europe more fitted by climate, soil and landholding structure to produce dairy products then the West Country. Therefore, if I trusted my judgement, and sought to benefit by the emerging political prospect, it seemed a good idea to buy as much land as I could afford, put up as many new dairies as the land would hold, and build up the dairy herd as fast as possible. Now, I thought, was the time to do it, for once our adhesion to the Common Market became an accomplished fact, land prices, cattle prices and building costs would rocket, and I would be unable to attempt the expansion I contemplated. I surmised that once membership was an accomplished fact, the established dairy farmers would be in a privileged position by reason of their prior investment, and it would be virtually impossible for newcomers to join them save by purchasing established enterprises. That was my hunch and I backed it with my shirt.

I remember a time in 1969, when reasonable farmland in our

area was selling for about £350 an acre, saying to John Thacker that I thought agricultural land would fetch £1,000 an acre by 1980. I was wrong, for it went to more than double that figure, but I was obviously thinking in the right direction.

In the event, Britain did not become self-sufficient in temperate-climate foods or even in dairy produce, as it ought to have done. This was to be illustrated in a somewhat surprising way after New Zealand Cheddar had been eased out of the domestic market. Its place was not taken up by the domestic product, as it could so easily have been, but by Irish, French, Dutch and German imports. The fault for this did not really lie with the British dairy industry but with the British government. A climate for expansion is given to an industry when a price structure for its products is such as to allow for a healthy profit out of which investment in modern equipment and for expansion can be made. Without that, relatively few people will want to risk investment to produce a product whose price is deliberately kept low by government price-fixing and whose volume is kept down by regulations, and where encouragement is given to foreign exporters to dump their produce on the home market as a means of keeping down prices.

Successive British governments, forever worrying about the consumer, and forever playing the electoral game, never gave British farmers the price support required to generate the massive increase in dairy and meat production which would have made us self-sufficient in these foods and encouraged a strong export trade in them in those years prior to our entry into the Common Market; and a great opportunity was largely thrown away.

CHAPTER 6

Cheesemaking

By 1970 I had come to realize that the profits from dairying, however one increased the size of one's enterprise with the object of using one's fixed assets to the hilt, were limited. I cannot be dogmatic, as farm college lecturers and textbooks like to be, about the percentage of return on capital employed, because this depends so much on when one spends one's capital for land purchase, builds one's dairies, buys or rears one's herds, and how one treats such things as capital depreciation and appreciation of land values. It was generally thought that a well-managed farm could produce a profit of about 4 per cent on capital employed, and many farm enterprises that were not properly geared to large-scale wheat or barley growing, or dairying, or specialized fruit and vegetable production, probably did a lot worse. It was a good deal less than was expected from a well-run industrial enterprise, and nothing like what could be got from successful property development and many a service industry.

This probably explains the lack of enthusiasm in any of the main political parties for land nationalisation. Land nationalisation would result either in such a colossal investment by government in farming that it would starve all other forms of investment in industry and services, or in under-investment, general neglect and a phenomenal run-down in production. We can see from the performance of Communist countries in agriculture that it is the latter alternative that actually occurs.

Quite simply, many people prefer being their own master, and living a rural life, to earning a big salary in a crowded city, and are prepared to accept a much lower return on their capital and reward for their labour and enterprise if they can live as independent farmers on their own land.

In business terms, I did not regard the return on investment as satisfactory and I started to think about additional ways we might treat our principal primary product, which was milk, so that it would earn more for us.

I considered various possibilities, including milk-retailing and manufacturing ice-cream, yoghourt and butter. None of these attracted me, for I felt either the field was too crowded or the market too susceptible to sudden change. It was cheesemaking that seemed our best option. First of all, Britain at that time produced only 38 per cent of the cheese it consumed, so that it seemed then that there would be no hindrance to a modest increase in domestic production. Secondly, it seemed a type of investment similar to dairying in that, provided one made a solid contribution to building and equipment and conducted the enterprise carefully, one could rely on a moderate but steady return on one's capital and efforts. Thirdly, it was a natural adjunct to dairying, particularly in the neighbouring county of Somerset, where many dairy farms had been harnessed to cheese production for a long time past.

Having arrived at a decision in principle, it was necessary to decide what cheese to make. I believe that I first thought of making Dorset Blue Vinny, a low-fat blue cheese, but the difficulty of production and the uncertainty of marketing it put me off the idea, and my thoughts turned to Cheddar. It was natural that they should, since Somerset, less than an hour's drive away, was the centre of Cheddar production. Other points in Cheddar's favour were that it happened to be, by a long chalk, the most popular cheese eaten in Britain; that it could be stored for a considerable time, and up to a point improved with age; and that there was a good deal of expertise available for its manufacture.

When I told John Thacker and Reg Jones of my intentions, I was met by silence. Then they endeavoured to dissuade me. 'Why not be content with the way things were going and continue doing what we had embarked on so successfully?' was their attitude. I understood the reason for their thinking. John was at home with cattle and with farming folk. He knew nothing about cheesemaking and the quasi-factory men on whom we would have to rely, and realized that the enterprise, if it ever got off the ground, would be out of his control, and could damage or even wreck the farming enterprise if it were mismanaged. Reg Jones had never seen a cheese dairy, let alone built one, and could only regard the putative enterprise with apprehension.

I reckoned differently. I had not known anything about dairying or any other kind of farming five years before, and yet here I was in charge of a growing and potentially profitable dairy estate. If one wished to enter a new field and was prepared to make the necessary investment, attract the men with the skills required, and buckle down and study the process of manufacture and that of marketing the produce one made, why not do it?

A start was made. We got in touch with a Miss Newall from the Ministry of Agriculture at Wells and on Guy Fawkes day in 1971 she visited us and discussed the mysteries of Cheddar cheesemaking. Mysterious was the right description for the entire process. First of all, we would have to get permission from the Milk Marketing Board, to whom we had to sell our milk, to buy it back from them for further processing. Then, if it was Farmhouse Cheddar we wished to make, we would have to join the Farmhouse Cheesemakers Association in Wells. They were understandably careful about whom they allowed to join them, and in general did not welcome new applicants, particularly those without a cheesemaking past. If we surmounted these obstacles we would need a skilled cheesemaker, two assistants and perhaps a woman to clean up. Miss Newall thought that the buildings and plant might cost £50,000 and that there was perhaps a penny profit in every pound of cheese made. It also seemed that it was usual to keep pigs with a cheese dairy, since they were the means of disposing of the otherwise unwanted by-product, whey.

The next step was to invite the Planning Officer over to discuss where the cheese dairy and piggery would be built. It was decided that the dairy could be situated just north of Parks Farm and the piggery 100 yards west of it in a hollow masked by hedges on our western boundary. The Ministry were paying 40 per cent grant on buildings at that time, which was satisfactory. Then on 30 December 1971, Miss Newall came along with Miss Maddever, a Cornishwoman of about sixty with silver hair and bright blue eyes. She was the Senior Advisory Officer of the Ministry on Cheddar Cheesemaking and was supposed to know most of what there was to know about the subject. I asked her to supervise the lay-out of the cheese dairy and advise Reg Jones, who was now getting on with plans and specifications for it. She too was vague about the profitability of cheesemaking. It seemed that there had been about sixty cheesemakers in the Farmhouse Cheesemakers Association but that an unprofitable period had resulted in a considerable fall-out of makers, of whom there were only about thirty now, so the time might not be unpropitious for applying to join them.

ASHLEY CHASE: *A Dorset Domain*

The following day I telephoned Roger Metcalf of the Milk Marketing Board to find out if they would let me have my own milk for the enterprise. He talked of perhaps letting me have 800 gallons a day but mentioned that the Ministry seemed more in favour of boosting the production of 'mousetrap' Cheddar than the better quality product which the Farmhouse Cheesemakers Association existed to promote and market. On 17 January 1972, he telephoned to say that permission had been given to me to process 250,000 gallons of milk into cheese for the first year. As the allocation for the year would start in the following September and I intended to start making cheese by January 1973, that envisaged a milk yield of about 1,000 gallons a day. I was so pleased about it, and so inexperienced, that I did not realize that I had been given a licence to lose money, unless that allocation was considerably increased thereafter, because 250,000 gallons of milk spaced out on an entire year worked out at only 700 gallons a day, which was far too little on which to run a brand-new cheese dairy with the latest equipment and adequate staff, and make a profit.

The first cheese dairy I went to see was just over the border in Somerset. I visited it one Winter's day with John and Reg. The buildings were ramshackle and the equipment antiquated. It was cold and dark, and it pelted while we were there. Pigs were kept too, and the sight of them rolling around in the mud created by the rain and their own excrement filled me with disgust. It was the very picture of a squalid and moribund farm, and when the owner said that there was no profit in cheesemaking, we were all inclined to agree and I was half-inclined to give up the idea. But then I noticed, by the side of a barn, a rather splendid-looking Jaguar, and it made me think that however depressed things might then be in the cheesemaking world, it had not always been so, and might change for the better in the future.

Cheesemaking

We decided to look at another enterprise, larger and more modern, and went to see Andrew Warren's cheese dairy at Coombe Farm near Crewkerne. That was an entirely different affair. Starting as a farm bailiff, Andrew Warren had built up a network of farm partnerships with dairies that supplied him with milk, and he was then processing 10,000 gallons of milk daily into Farmhouse Cheddar. We saw the process of cheesemaking with the best equipment then available to a farmhouse cheesemaker, and we saw cream and butter being made too. Yet I was nearly put off here too, although for entirely different reasons. It was not the squalor and dilapidated look of the place this time, but its size, and modernity, the numbers of huge lorries and tankers trundling in and out, and the number of people working there. I counted at least fifteen. This involved a far larger commitment of capital and a far bigger enterprise than I had anticipated for a venture that I could not help but think would be experimental for a considerable time to come. But Reg Jones pointed out that many of the vehicles I saw were employed for moving produce in and out, for Andrew Warren bought and sold other farm commodities on a considerable scale; and others must be tankers bringing in the large percentage of milk he drew in from his co-operators. Andrew Warren was kind and helpful, but vague about the profit he made, and tended rather to put me off insisting on being a farmhouse cheesemaker. He said that there must be more profitable and less risky ways of investing capital. Looking back, I am sure he was right, but as my aim was to build up a large model dairy estate, this was not a contention to which I paid too much notice.

I was soon accepted by the Ministry of Agriculture and the Farmhouse Cheesemakers Association as a cheesemaker. The cheese dairy was being built and the equipment had been ordered and I was getting skilled advice. All I lacked was the staff to make the cheese, and above all, a head cheesemaker. Such a man was not easy to come by. It was not much use taking on a man from a big creamery, since their method of making cheese was so different from that of a farmhouse cheesemaker that he simply would not be suitable for the job. The head cheesemakers within the scheme numbered no more than thirty and there was little reason why a competent man should leave his secure job to obtain employment in a new venture run by people without any experience of cheesemaking and its trials. My best hope lay in finding a competent chief assistant who was ready to take off and run a cheese dairy himself. That was precisely what happened, thanks to Commander Streatfeild.

The Commander, who was Managing Director of the farming partnership of Streatfeild Hood, near Bridport, also ran the only farmhouse cheesemaking dairy in Dorset. He was a remarkable man, built in an heroic mould. He had had expectations of reaching high rank in the Royal Navy, but had been attacked by cancer in his early thirties and forced to retire. That had not deterred him from starting a new career in farming, and in partnership with Lord Hood he had built up a thriving farming estate in West Dorset with dairies, a cheesemaking enterprise and a large piggery. We were to co-operate in carting our milk to our respective cheese dairies one day, and to become friends. It was an indication of the vitality of the man, and the variety of his interests, that when he died many years later, over 700 mourners packed the church at Symondsbury and flowed out into the churchyard.

Having heard of my requirements, he recommended his own chief assistant cheesemaker, Mike Harp, to us. He reckoned that Mike was competent to be a head cheesemaker, but that if he waited for the succession at Denhay, where their cheese dairy was, it might be a long time before he achieved his promotion. So he introduced us to him and we took him on at the end of 1972. It was necessary for him to go for a few weeks' course at Cannington before he joined us, because Streatfeild Hood made round traditional cheese and we had decided to make block cheese. The traditional cheese has a rind and can be stored for a long period, from one to three years. As a result, if well-made, it can develop a strong flavour, guaranteed to satisfy the most discriminating gourmet; but its production is labour-intensive and ties up a lot of capital for quite a time as it matures in store. It had now fallen out of favour with many of the supermarkets, who preferred a rindless rectangular 40 lb block that could be consumer-packed. Such a block was a more reliable way of making a very acceptable Cheddar, and much easier to transport and store.

Supermarkets often decide what we shall eat, and how our food comes to us, and their power in the cheese-marketing world is shown by the fact that cylindrical cheeses now form no more than 10 per cent of the cheese produced by the Farmhouse Cheesemakers Association, which itself produces only about 10 per cent of the Cheddar made in this country. We had decided to play safe and go along with the supermarkets' requirements, so Mike had to take a course on cutting, wrapping and boxing before he was ready to start production. He brought with him his wife, Dorothy, a competent butter-maker and reliable assistant, and she proved a tower of strength to him in the new enterprise.

The cheese dairy with its equipment cost me nearly £100,000, but when built it was the last word in modernity for a farmhouse cheesemaker, and formed a marked contrast with the establishments of many of the cheesemakers of long standing whose equipment was a strange mixture of the modern and the picturesquely antique. In the end I had decided against having a piggery. The economics of it put me off. Its purpose would have been to utilize the whey from the cheese dairy, a product that could have provided a quarter of the pigs' rations at virtually no cost; but a piggery to take up such quantities of whey would have cost over £60,000, with another £200,000 more to spend if I ever developed the cheese capacity for which I was hoping. The turnover in pigs and pig-food would have become colossal. Moreover, there is an old farming adage about pigs: they are either copper or gold. The transition can take place from one season to the next, because it is very easy for a surplus to develop and for the market to be inundated with imports. I was daunted by the prospect. It seemed to me to be a case of the tail wagging the dog. I decided that I had quite enough on my plate for the time being in starting an expensive venture for making a product I knew little about, without simultaneously getting involved in what was potentially a still more expensive venture in a field which was notoriously risky and about which I was even more ignorant. So there were to be no pigs.

The sub-contractors were slow and the manufacturers of the dairy equipment also delayed. If ever the concept of time being of the essence had meant something in a contract with a British manufacturer, it had ceased to do so by 1973. We pushed here and cajoled there, but there was still delay. But eventually, on 14 February 1973, we began to make cheese at Ashley Chase. By June, we learned that most of our cheese made in February and March had been classified in Wells as fine grade. By July, 1,350 gallons of milk a day were passing into the cheese dairy.

In March, aware by then of the need to make more cheese if the enterprise was to prove profitable, I had applied to the Milk Marketing Board for permission to make more. I met with resistance. There was a need, they said, to restrict cheesemaking for the next two years to accommodate the New Zealand, Irish and Continental Cheddar pouring into the country. In some respects I am a fairly simple man. I did not then understand the necessity of deliberately hampering home production for the benefit of the importer any more than I understand it now, but I saw that it was not for me to argue against the higher forms of economic lunacy. I simply invited some of the MMB officials down to Ashley Chase to see the new cheese dairy in operation, told them what I had spent on it, and relied on their decency.

They relented and doubled my Cheddar datum for the following year to 500,000 gallons of milk, provided it all came from my own dairies. That meant I could keep up a daily average of 1,350 gallons which, roughly speaking, would enable me to make 1,350 lb of Cheddar a day, or 240 tons a year. We had been fairly launched as farmhouse cheesemakers.

CHAPTER 7

The Crisis and Further Expansion

There were various reasons prompting me to expand my dairying estate, as it had now become. After the successful launching of Parks, Ashley and Lower Kingston Russell Dairies, it was evident that dairying suited West Dorset admirably, and was in fact the one enterprise we could rely on to bring in a steady income and a profit at the end of the year. Beef rearing, as an offshoot of dairying, supplemented profits but could not be relied on as the main enterprise; nor could sheep, as we had found out. Wheat or barley growing were not reliable either. There was too much mist about, and the Summers were too uncertain to bank on heavy crops year after year, although sometimes one could expect 50 cwt an acre, a reasonable if not spectacular yield in those days.

I was carried away by the conviction that we were on the verge of a price explosion which would be set in motion the moment it seemed certain we would enter the Common Market. The price of everything would rocket when that happened, and only the larger enterprises would survive, except for those family farms which employed virtually no hired labour and relied wholly on members of the family.

That was one inducement to buy land, build dairies and houses, and lay on roads, electricity, drainage and water.

When I started a cheesemaking industry, a second inducement manifested itself. For it was quickly made clear to me that I would only be allowed to make Cheddar from the milk my own dairies produced, and that I would not be able to buy in milk from other producers. This meant that the cheese dairy could only be profitable if I expanded my milking parlours, which entailed buying more land, building more dairies, and buying or breeding more cows. Therefore, some time in 1969, I set myself a target, and that was to have 1,000 cows to produce about 1,200,000 gallons of milk a year, within the next three or four years. From then on John Thacker and I were intermittently inspecting farms from the coast north to Bulbarrow, and from Tolpuddle to Bridport and beyond. We looked for farms that had suitable ground and a sensibly arranged lay-out and buildings together with enough cottages for us to install properly run dairies with competent staff. They also had to be near enough for us to transport their milk to our cheese dairy, which in fact meant a thirty- to forty-minute drive by a tractor-drawn milk-tanker.

We were not having too much luck in obtaining these requirements until John learnt that Harry Stott, the elderly owner of the 540-acre Higher Kingston Russell Farm, with land on both sides of the A35, was thinking of retirement. He had no children and was therefore contemplating a sale. He had a large Queen Anne house, four cottages that had been erected by a former Duke of Bedford, and a 120-cow dairy. It was really out of our valley, and yet no more than a ten-minute drive away from where the cheese dairy at Parks was being built. It was in fact barely a half-mile away, as the crow flies, from our Lower Kingston Russell Farm.

John started to negotiate with him in February 1972 but immediately ran into difficulties. Stott did and yet did not seem to want to sell. He had been there fifty years and was understandably reluctant to leave. A further difficulty was the necessity to buy or build a retirement house to move into when he had sold Higher Kingston Russell Farm. So negotiations dragged on.

Eventually Harry Stott decided to sell the property by auction. We were then caught up and influenced by political factors and a wholly unexpected extraneous factor that combined to transform the whole position.

What is the difference between a difficulty and a crisis? A difficulty is something one can foresee and can overcome without recourse to special reserves of energy and resources. A crisis is something that cannot be foreseen, that hits you out of the blue, and will sink you unless you are able to summon up resources of spirit you are unaware of having, and sometimes material resources that you are unaware of possessing.

A good example of a difficulty is the trouble we experienced over the anti-brucellosis campaign which the Ministry of Agriculture began in 1967. Brucellosis is a contagious disease which may cause abortion and in some cases infertility, thus reducing milk yield. It has a further characteristic, in that it can be passed on to humans through touch or drinking milk or milk products which have not been pasteurised. It used to be almost an occupational disease for veterinary surgeons dealing with cattle. Its symptoms had some affinity with those relating to malaria: recurring fever with a high temperature, swollen glands, pains in the head, the thighs or the stomach, coupled with debility. It was often mistaken for glandular fever, or Summer flu. It was unpleasant, weakening and, in some cases, fatal. We had personal reasons to know of it since before we ever came to Ashley Chase,

The Crisis and Further Expansion

Cedric had developed these very symptoms. For five years doctors and child specialists had diagnosed the symptoms as those of glandular fever, and then one day I saw a description of brucellosis in a farm paper and asked our doctor to test for it. After some resistance he did, and it turned out to be the trouble. The remedy was a course of the antibiotic Imperacin, but after five years it took rather longer to be effective than it would have been had the disease been treated immediately it was contracted.

The Ministry planned to tackle the problem in the same way that they had earlier virtually eradicated tuberculosis from herds. A voluntary campaign was started with the aim of ensuring that herds were made clean. If a herd passed three successive tests without reactors being found in it, it became a 'clean' herd, and stayed clean, and its numbers had to be recruited from heifers born of clean herds. If a single cow in a herd of say 100 cows 'reacted', it was removed to another 'dirty' herd or sold for slaughter, and the whole herd remained dirty until every cow in it had passed three tests successfully.

Realizing that the scheme would eventually be made compulsory, we voluntarily joined it in the Summer of 1971 when we had three herds, Parks, Ashley and Lower Kingston Russell. One owner was allowed to have both clean and dirty herds however, even on the same farm if they and their progeny were kept completely apart. We knew that the Parks herd was a dirty one, so we decided to move any cow that failed the test to Parks until March 1972, when the Parks herd would be sold and the dairy building thoroughly cleaned and fumigated, and then converted to a beef unit.

By October 1971 Ashley had been closed for cleaning and fumigation and a few months later had begun to be built up as a clean herd. Then in October 1971 we began testing at our biggest dairy, Lower Kingston Russell, which then had about 160 cows. Twenty-seven of them reacted at the first test. By November 100 cows on the estate had reacted and our daily gallonage was down to 670 after having been 800.

In April 1972 only two cows had failed at Lower Kingston Russell and by January 1973 they had all passed. By June they all passed a second test, and yet, in the following July, four failed although they had passed tests twenty-two times. By October 1973 we withdrew from the scheme, which meant that we could go on running Lower Kingston Russell as a dirty herd provided it was rigidly separated from the others. Withdrawal implied that the herd would gradually dwindle until we sold it, cleaned and fumigated the premises, and bought in a clean herd.

The odd thing was that none of those Lower Kingston Russell cows ever aborted their calves, so they must have had brucellosis in a pretty mild form. We could never understand how a whole herd could pass a test twice and then have one or more cows go down. Was the bug in the buildings? Was the after-birth of infected cows on the estate? Was it brought in by birds or foxes? I had a suspicion that the cows never had brucellosis but that what registered was the remains of the S27 serum they were given for inoculation. Whatever the truth of the matter, it was an expensive business, because there was usually the difference of £120 between a cow sold from a dirty herd and a brucellosis-tested cow bought from a clean herd. By 1976 we finally cleared Lower Kingston Russell, which by then was down to 120 cows, cleaned it out, and three months later replaced it with a clean herd which was quickly built up.

By the time the 200-strong Litton herd had been built up, the 100-cow Ashley herd was milking, and new herds had been built up elsewhere. A great difficulty had been met, and at much expense, overcome.

Mike and Dorothy Harp starting the cheddaring after the whey has drained from the curd

The slabs of curd are milled and the salt added before being pressed into 40 lb blocks

The rotary milking parlour at Roman Road Dairy

Heifers eating silage in their specially-designed pens at West Hill

The Crisis and Further Expansion

In 1972 I experienced a full-scale crisis arising from the sudden sharp increase in the value of farmland. In June 1970 the Conservatives had romped home to a convincing electoral victory under Edward Heath. I did not know much about Heath save that he was thoroughly committed to bringing the country into the Common Market and therefore, in my estimate, to lifting the deadening hand of Socialism once and for all from the country's back. I remember staying up on the night of 18 June to watch the first half-dozen election results come in. They showed a 6 per cent swing to the Conservatives, which were it to be more or less the same throughout the country, indicated that there would be a Conservative government with a working majority. In the flush of the moment I promised Colette a fur coat, and immediately raised the allowances of the boys.

General de Gaulle had meanwhile relinquished power in 1969. No sooner had Heath assumed power than he went off to negotiate our entry into the Market. Pompidou, de Gaulle's successor, offered no objection and it was merely a question of our accepting the terms held out to us. These were more difficult to accept than they would have been had we applied to join before de Gaulle came to power, but had they been twice as onerous as they proved to be, we would have accepted them. There were no really viable alternatives left to us. By the summer of 1972 it was beginning to be obvious that the UK would join the Common Market and by midnight on 31 December our adhesion to the Treaty of Rome became effective. Agricultural land prices had begun to be affected from the beginning of that year.

When our negotiations started with Stott in February 1972 I thought his farm was worth between £350 and £400 an acre. By June there were less potentially profitable farms, not too far away, going for £800 an acre. By the time I went up to the Royal

ASHLEY CHASE: *A Dorset Domain*

Agricultural Show on 5 July, Richard Thorpe was telling me that £700 an acre was the very least a reasonable farm would fetch. Later that month I inspected the 1,330-acre Hedge End Estate near Bulbarrow, which could have been bought for £300 an acre. It was a great prairie 700 feet high, and would have needed £100 an acre to fence it and put up adequate buildings on it. There might have been times in Winter when it would have been impossible to get the milk out, and I turned it down. In retrospect, I am sure that I made a mistake to do so. By August Ensors, the local land agents, were telling us that they were being asked to quote £1,000 an acre for a ninety-acre farm, and that they had no idea of land values any more. By 24 October the 2,000-odd acres of the Candover Estate in Hampshire, which a few days earlier had been sold for £1,350 an acre, were resold to Ronald Lyon, the builder, for £1,400 an acre. What I had expected to happen one day had suddenly occurred in a mere nine months, and at a most awkward time for me.

And then, as the auction date for the sale of Higher Kingston Russell Farm was delayed for week after week, another factor, totally unforeseen by me, began to make its importance felt.

I was in the habit of receiving friends and family at Ashley Chase, showing them the latest developments and expatiating on the delights of living in the country and farming the land. More than one family as a result followed my example, although in a lesser way. I used also to recommend my land agents to them, if they were interested. In our earlier days Bernard Thorpe and Partners had not merely seen to our accounts; they had also given us farming advice in general, and of course done the annual stock-take.

In those early days they assigned to us a relatively new graduate from a farming college who had never farmed for himself but was full of the latest theories and practices as taught in farm colleges. He came down several times to offer us advice, as well as to value our livestock. It was only when, in the opinion of John and myself, he overvalued our sheep at the end of a trading year, which in my view had the effect of disguising the loss we were making on the sheep venture, that I decided we did not need academic advice, and could more safely rely on the more practical experience of my own management staff.

Early in September, I learned that a close friend had inspected Higher Kingston Russell in the company of this gentleman, and that she too was interested in it. She was a timid person whose mind was set on that particular farm simply because it was close to mine and in a familiar part of the country, but her interest could well have induced the selling agent further to postpone the auction, encouraged by the prospect of rival bidders. I rang up Bernard Thorpe and Partners in some alarm and asked if it was really possible for one segment of their firm to be negotiating for me to acquire a farm, while another of their offices, unaware of what was going on, was negotiating to buy the same farm on behalf of someone to whom I had introduced them. After some enquiries, it transpired that this was quite possible, and was in fact being done, and that the very employee who had previously been assigned to advise us on farming matters was the man who had accompanied the interested parties. He had of course done so in all innocence, but when I fully realized what was going on, I asked Richard to withdraw from acting for my friend, which he promptly did when the circumstances were brought to his attention.

This did not prevent my friend from engaging another agent and pursuing the matter, as she was perfectly entitled to do. This faced me with a terrible problem. Higher Kingston Russell Farm was only half a mile from us and it made excellent sense to me to buy it. I could only do so however by outbidding a close friend, whose intervention of course would have the effect of pushing up the price.

The auction eventually took place on 25 October and on that day I and John Thacker met Reg Jones and another partner of his, Tony Witham, in Puddletown for lunch. I felt pretty gloomy but cheered up when I was told of the possibility that an institution might purchase the freehold and lease it back to me on the basis of a 2 per cent return. We arranged that we would sit together and that Jones should bid up to £750 an acre, which worked out at £394,000, after which I should bid. The husband of my friend had retreated to the comfort of the King's Head, but had deputed his agent, Laland, to bid for him.

The auction was held in the Dorchester Town Hall, and I positioned myself by the window from where I could see Laland and the auctioneer quite clearly. The bidding started at 3.30 pm and in no time at all Jones had dropped out of the bidding, and I was left to start waving my hand. A third bidder joined in the fray, and took the price up to £480,000 or £920 an acre. Then it became a duel between Laland and me.

It was the kind of situation that auctioneers love to see happen. The bidding went over £500,000 and Reg Jones was almost floored with emotion, while John could not bear to look at me. Laland went to £535,000, and my capping bid of £540,000 saw the property knocked down to me. I had paid an amazing £1,032 an acre.

People crowded around the aged Stott to congratulate him on the extraordinary sale he had achieved, as well they might, for he had sold his land for more than twice what he would have got for it ten months before. He merely commented that had his bailiff not refused to vacate his house to enable him to offer it with vacant possession, he would have got £1,500 more!

About thirty congratulatory telephone calls came through that night from people who preferred a local man to have secured the farm, but they whistled at the price. I was doing a certain amount of whistling myself by then, for turning to Witham after the auction and enquiring about the institution that might buy and lease back to me at 2 per cent, I was told that although their representatives were there, they were now talking about 3 per cent. The inference was that I would have to resell at a considerable loss if I wanted to lease-back.

All but 100 acres of Higher Kingston Russell was bounded by roads, except on the eastern side where a thin strip of eight acres of gorse lay between the farm and the road. It was supposed to be full of foxes and their lairs, and was much valued by the local hunt. As it abutted the side where we had determined to build a new dairy, I decided it would be best to buy it to round out the property. It was owned by Lady Williams whose husband's family, centred on Bridehead House, had owned the land since the Napoleonic Wars. She refused an offer for it but agreed instead to sell the 392-acre farm of which it formed part. Early in 1973 therefore I contracted to buy West Hill Farm for £820 an acre, which was a pretty full price for land without houses or buildings, save for a small nineteenth-century barn. That purchase gave me a solid block of land with good soil, measuring a mile and a half long and averaging a mile broad and covering an area of 915 acres. I had to do something with it to justify the expense and to bring in a decent return, and therefore determined to build what would then be the largest dairy in Dorset on the site.

I had also by then determined to keep the freeholds of the two farms, and borrow from the Agricultural Mortgage Corporation to pay for them.

The fourteen months ending in February 1973 was in retrospect

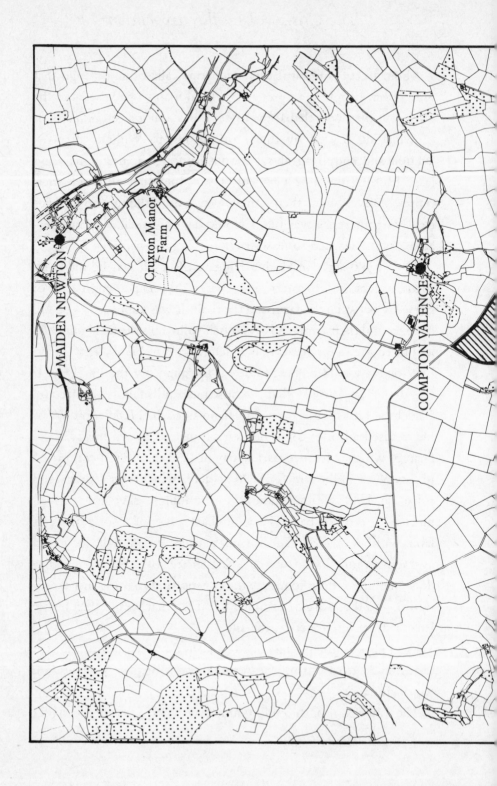

MAIDEN NEWTON

Cruxton Manor
Farm

COMPTON VALENCE

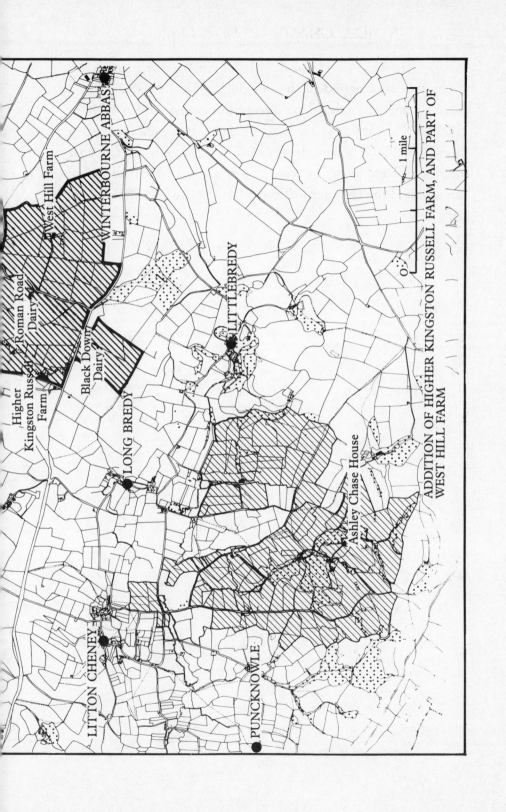

WEST HILL FARM

Higher
Kingston Russell
Farm

Roman Road

Dairy

Black Down
Dairy

West Hill Farm

WINTERBOURNE ABBAS

LITTLEBREDY

LONG BREDY

Ashley Chase House

LITTON CHENEY

PUNCKNOWLE

0   1 mile

ADDITION OF HIGHER KINGSTON RUSSELL FARM, AND PART OF
WEST HILL FARM

the most critical period of the building up of the Ashley Chase Estate. It saw me increase the acreage of my estate from 1,410 to 2,325 acres, complete a new 225-cow dairy, build and complete a cheese dairy with a capacity for making 1,000 tons of Cheddar cheese a year and bring my dairies up to a total of 430 cows. I had also acquired the land needed to expand the dairies to hold 1,000 dairy cows.

CHAPTER *8*

Hell for Leather

I can foresee critics of this book complaining that for a work that professes to relate how an agricultural estate was built up, it contains an inordinate amount of politics. I do not apologize for bringing in what some people might find distasteful, because politics form the framework within which farming, industry and commerce operate.

If one government decides to legislate for a cheap-food policy based on imports, and another government then acts in a way designed to switch us to a dear-food policy based on self-sufficiency, the farming interest will either way be vitally affected. It will also be vitally affected if a government suddenly throws all financial discretion to the winds, distorts the value of money and acts in a way that is guaranteed to destroy the whole basis of financial credit on which so much of commerce and industry rests.

Edward Heath has one solid achievement to his credit: he brought us into the Common Market. For the rest, his Ministry was a shambles. Of course, he had bad luck, but he seems also to have had the gift of compounding it with bad judgement. He brought in as Chancellor of the Exchequer Anthony Barber, who looked and sounded on television the nicest man one could hope to meet. To the old question, 'Is this a man from whom you would buy a second-hand car?', you would unhesitatingly have replied 'Yes', and you might have gone further and commiserated with him on the need to sell it. Therefore when, in 1972, he brought in a Budget which allowed the banks to extend credit by 20 per cent under the slogan 'Dash for Growth', many of the so-called experts gave him the benefit of the doubt in knowing what he was doing. The argument was that with this extra money in circulation, the banks would have more to lend and industrialists would be able to borrow to modernize their plant and increase production, which would leap forward to such an extent as to justify the addition to the money supply by an equivalent addition to the gross national product. It was a naïve assumption. It omitted to take into account the fact that few British industrialists had undertakings capable of boosting their production. Many were only nominally in charge of their own work forces. Their real masters were the union bosses who were dedicated to inflating their Union membership, which in turn involved gross over-manning, low productivity, reducing markets, low profits, often ending in no profits at all, and insolvency. In such circumstances fresh capital was unlikely to be attracted there. It was much more likely to be attracted to activities which were not dominated by the power of the big unions, such as farming and the redevelopment of antiquated city centres and office accommodation.

Printing money on this scale in these circumstances had two main consequences. The first was to push up wage rates by an equivalent percentage, increase the price of food and consumer goods, and send up land prices and interest rates. The rate of increase of such things rose to between 20 per cent and 30 per cent per annum. The second was to increase investment in redeveloping urban centres, which seemed the one type of investment where returns appeared to be able to keep pace with inflationary costs. It was not long before left-wing journalists began to agitate against what they deemed to be inordinate profits being made in the construction and redevelopment industries. The climate of opinion, a hangover from the first Attlee government, was rather against profits. They were regarded as somehow anti-social. Chairmen whose fortunate lot it was to announce good profits did so almost apologetically, for it was tantamount to an admission that they were not paying their employees adequately. It was almost fashionable to announce losses and call for government money to bail out industries.

In an attempt to stave off criticism, the troika which then dictated government fiscal policy, Edward Heath, Anthony Barber and James Prior, determined to torpedo the property industry by imposing a ban on all rent increases on business properties, which term included shops, offices and factories. It was very effective. Many well-run property companies and great trading empires were forced into mergers, or bankruptcy. There were a few suicides. A combination of an inflation running at 20 per cent per annum, extraordinarily high interest rates, a falling pound and, now, a bar against their keeping rents abreast of inflation, was enough to destroy them. Their fate often had little to do with the quality of their management; it simply depended on how they had extended themselves in the pursuit of expansion when the government-planned blows hit them.

In the midst of this economic chaos, the Yom Kippur War broke out, and the Arab oil states, to avenge themselves for their humiliating defeat by the Israelis and to hit out at the West, increased their oil price fourfold. It was a classic case of the consumer being held to ransom by a cartel formed to run up the price of a necessary commodity. In a former age it would have been met by an expeditionary force sent out to knock sense into the heads of the natives. In 1973 that method of controlling commodity prices was deemed outdated. The result was a world-wide depression, a further spur to inflation, a phenomenal increase in wealth of the Arab oil states, and, eventually, the exploitation of the reserves of oil and gas in the North Sea. Other countries in the West coped with this increase in inflation by prudent moves designed to limit the damage. Our government simply compounded the problems with their 'Dash for Growth' policy, which was nearly as disastrous to us as Mao's 'Great Leap Forward' was to China.

The seventies also witnessed the rise of the take-over specialist. A group of City financiers, with the backing of merchant banks, would start buying up businesses with no long-term wish to run them, but with the idea of selling off individual parts or the real property associated with it. The public was told that the purpose of these purchases was to substitute superior management and build up the business. This of course was usually so much hogwash.

We had an example of it right under our eyes. Sharp Tone were a firm of tractor repairers, and the moment we had a tractor breakdown, a telephone call would bring their mechanics speedily to the field where the disabled farm vehicle lay. In 1966 Sharp Tone were acquired by the Reeves Group, and within six months the Bridport branch was shut down. Our reaction was swift. Their two best mechanics, Ron Gurd and Barry Dare, were soon on our payroll and a large tractor-repair shed was erected to house them and their working implements. As the farming infrastructure around us began to diminish, we simply supplied a larger and larger part of it.

The Conservatives lost both the general elections in 1974 and the country staggered on under their no less incompetent successors. By November 1974 there were rumours that, in addition to those banks being succoured by the Bank of England, even one of the 'Big Five' clearing banks was teetering on the brink of insolvency. Although this was denied, we shall never know how close the bank came to it. The cause was simple enough. The bulk of its securities was land and the buildings on it. At a time when inflation was running at such a high rate, legislation had decreed that the increased nominal value that inflation had added to the properties pledged to banks was to be transferred from the owners of business property to their tenants. Looked at another way, the banks as mortgagees were losing the securities for their loans at the rate of 20 to 30 per cent per annum. Two or three years of that kind of thing, and most of their loans would have been effectively irrecoverable. The Conservative government, in its anxiety to hit the property developers, had devised a policy which was guaranteed to bring the entire banking system crashing down. It is to the credit of the Labour government, and particularly, it is said, of Lord Lever, the Chancellor of the Duchy of Lancaster, who had formed some link between the government and the City, that this absurd legislation was abruptly repealed in December 1974.

This was the financial background in the shadow of which I was attempting to build up a large farming estate on borrowed money. I was doing the wrong thing, yet I was committed to it. I could not tell what new folly the government of the day would perpetrate. They seemed committed to higher and higher degrees of inflation. In that event, one of the only safe things to hold was agricultural land, provided it was not leased out and one was not buying it at inflated prices. It seemed that we were heading towards national bankruptcy and that one might see occur in Britain the kind of inflation that Germany saw in 1923 when an egg could cost 1,000,000,000 marks. In the end the International Monetary Fund stepped in and saved us from that catastrophe.

They gradually shepherded us back to the world of financial commonsense, as they might have done to a Central American banana republic. But in 1973 and 1974 that world of relative stability did not exist. All accepted financial criteria had gone by the board. The ground quaked beneath my feet, as it must have quaked for many others.

Despite all this, 1973 was for us a year for planning as well as building. We had now completed the cheese dairy, just as a year before we had completed the 220-cow Litton Dairy with two new cottages. This year we began stocking up the dairy at Higher Kingston, partly with Ayrshires we had bought from Stott and partly with Friesians we had bred or bought elsewhere. We had increased our cow population from 300 to 500 by the end of 1973, and our milk yield from 334,000 to 358,000 gallons. Our aim now was to prepare plans to increase the number of cows in our herds to 800 within the next two years.

In March 1973 I had contracted with Lady Williams to buy West Hill Farm, though I was not due to complete the purchase till the following September; but with Lady Williams's permission, we took possession at once.

There was only one consideration which, in my view, could justify me taking on an extra one and a half square miles of farmland at that juncture, and that was to build up my cow population, and the milk and cheese revenues that would accompany it, as quickly as possible. So, before the Spring of 1973 was over, we were planning to build what we thought would be the largest dairy in Dorset. It would have covered cubicles for 262 cows with covered barns large enough to hold 2,400 tons of silage, calving and bull-pens, and a milking parlour big enough to milk twenty cows at a time.

It had at first been projected for the eastern edge of Higher

Kingston Russell Farm, but with the acquisition of West Hill Farm, it would now be in the very centre of the great new block of land I had just bought. During that Summer of 1973, Reg Jones prepared plans for the erection of the new dairy and the building of two cottages for the men who would operate it. By February 1974 we had cleared the planners, and the foundations of the dairy were being dug. They rested on the chalk which had been uncovered on a huge site, 250 yards long and 200 yards broad.

Simultaneously we began to bore for water about a mile away. Except for some houses and a small dairy in the south-west corner of this block of land, and a tiny nineteenth-century hay-barn, there was nothing but grass and sky. Everything, therefore, had to be brought to the site, including water, electricity and telephone.

The search for water began in a very old-fashioned way by bringing in a water-diviner. He walked around with a hazel wand in his hand until he came to a spot at the lower end of a combe at the eastern end of West Hill, when the wand began to shake violently. We accordingly bored for water where indicated, and at 300 feet beneath the surface struck into an underground channel which produced 5,000 gallons of water an hour; quite sufficient for the needs of the dairy we were erecting.

The two cottages we were building for the two new dairymen were subject to the permission of the Planning Committee for West Dorset and we had to conform to their nonsensical decrees. My intention was to build these three-bedroom cottages in stone, a local product commonly used in that part of Dorset. The Planning Committee however decreed that I should use brick as 'being more fit'. I had no time to argue with them. We had waited long enough for planning permission for the dairy and houses as it was. They had to be ready in time for the dairy whose in-calf heifers were already timed to start calving in the Autumn of 1974.

So I gave the order to build the houses in brick. Some time after they had been built, a Senior Planning Officer came to look at them. 'Splendid,' he said, 'but why did you build them in brick? Stone would have been more in keeping with this part of the country.'

We decided to break away from our policy of only building herringbone parlours, and to install a rotary parlour. Two or three years before we had gone to see a prototype of a rotary parlour on a farm near Okehampton in Devon. I went with John Thacker, Reg Jones and Reg Hardiman, a retired dairyman from Wimborne. The farm in which it had been installed was 700 feet up, the weather was freezing, and I remember how miserably cold we felt as we stood around in the observation room to watch proceedings. The yard was uncovered, the cake was delivered by a system we thought antique, and I remember, as a specially interesting feature of the operation, that the teat-cups had to be removed from the udders by hand, an operation that was obligingly performed by the farmer's mother. We had gone there to help make up our minds as to what type of milking parlour to install at our Litton dairy. As a result of what we saw on this hill farm, we quickly ordered an eight-a-side herringbone parlour for Litton.

But rotary parlours had improved a lot since then, and by the time we were ready to install one in our new dairy at Higher Kingston Russell, we were being offered a covered parlour with automatic cake-feed troughs, teat-cups that fell away from the udders when milking had finished, and a turntable on which twenty cows could stand and be fed and milked at the same time. Each cow, lured by the desire to eat and to have its udders relieved of milk, would step onto a slowly moving circular parlour. It then had its udders washed and was checked for condition. Its ration was fed into the troughs, the teat-cups were put on and milking

Louis and Colette with their sons Roby and Cedric

Sunset over the Bride Valley seen from Tenants Hill

The remains of St Luke's Chapel, built in the fourteenth century

The Restoration dancers in the courtyard

commenced. The circular parlour was driven by a half-horsepower motor. A full revolution took ten minutes and in that time twenty cows had been fed, washed, milked and checked for disease.

By October 1974 the buildings were ready. Ninety-five cows were being milked and the barns were full of silage. By January 1975, 200 cows were lying in the covered cubicles and being milked. We called this dairy Roman Road because it was built on a site only 200 yards from the old Roman road between Dorchester and the hill fort at Eggardon.

By April 1973 it was obvious that expansion on this scale would necessitate new buildings for heifers and calves. The site chosen was the upper end of the combe on West Hill Farm in which water had been found. At that time it was still covered with scrub. It was a splendid site for it faced south and was protected from the north-east winds by the sides of two hills. It was about three-quarters of a mile from the nearest road, so that use of it entailed the building of a new concrete road wide enough to carry tractors and trailers to the projected buildings. We had put up quite a number of buildings to house young stock, but these new ones were the best.

John got the idea for them from the home farm of the Ilchester Estate at Melbury House. They consisted of a long concrete wall, set in the face of the hill, with ten large enclosures facing south, the whole enclosed in walls for half their width. These enclosures were half roofed over and half open to the sky. They were separated from one another by galvanised iron gates which could swing open and enable the entire length of the cattle enclosure to be cleared quickly and easily by a muck-rake. Water was laid on at the back of each cubicle, and a long feeding trough ran along the front. The cattle pleased themselves where they lay, staying under cover when it rained and at night, and coming out in the sunshine. Each cubicle housed between eight and twelve cattle depending on size. We built two parallel lines of them, fifty yards apart. Up to 300 young cattle could be kept in them, and we never had cattle thrive as well as those at West Hill. Eighty yards in front of them, and lower down the combe, we built open cubicles for the larger cattle on a concrete pad. After a season we had these cubicles covered at shoulder height with corrugated iron, and 200 cattle wintered there eventually.

By 1974 this tract of land at West Hill, which had had nothing on it before but an old stone barn for 100 tons of hay, was supporting 500 young stock, lying in through the winter, and providing grazing for half a 250-cow dairy.

CHAPTER 9

Tied Cottages and Taxes

When I first started to farm in 1966, agricultural wages for a tractor driver or herdsman were about £11 a week. A dairyman might expect to earn a little more. This wage was considerably less than half that of a factory worker at the time. It was partly compensated for by provision of a rent-free house and, if one worked on a dairy farm, free milk. But the standard of living of those who worked on a farm was markedly lower than for those who worked in offices and factories, and had been so for a long time past. As a result, there was a continual exodus from the land to better-paid jobs in urban areas.

It is always rather difficult to measure the impact of inflation between one epoch and another because it is not uniform for all kinds of goods and services. The value of money fell by approximately eight times in the twenty years following 1966, but on that basis many things, particularly manufactured goods, may be relatively cheaper now than then. The average wage for agricultural workers, including bonuses for overtime, is about £130 a week, with dairymen, because of their special conditions, earning about £50 a week more, so that it would seem that they are, relatively speaking, at least 50 per cent better off now than then. I suspect that in real terms they may be better off than this rough and ready calculation implies. The biggest charge against their current income is the amount of tax they have to pay, which at the time of writing starts at 30 per cent after £35 a week for a single man, when one includes his National Insurance contributions, and amounts to an incredible imposition. This tax is regarded as so onerous that many men will refuse to work overtime because of their objection to paying one-third of their earnings to the State.

In 1966 few agricultural workers had motor cars and I doubt if any had colour television sets or washing machines. By 1986 most of them, save perhaps the rather elderly, had them. In 1966 it would have been safe to say that the only foreign travel any of them would have experienced would have been in wartime at HM Government's expense, or through a spell in the Merchant Navy in the adventurous days of their youth. Today, quite a few of them might be familiar with the Spanish coast or with Corfu. For the most part those who work at Ashley Chase live in three- or four-bedroomed cottages which, were they on the market as freeholds, would cost between £40-60,000. They have central heating, pay neither rent nor rates, and do not have to worry about maintaining their house. Of course, the house goes with the job, as for so many other occupations, but the need of the farmer for a competent man to live near the stock he tends is quite as great as that of the farmworker to have settled employment and a comfortable house, and if the farmer is unable to offer a suitable house he is unlikely to attract a suitable farmworker.

The farmworker has other advantages not offered to those who work in town. He is saved the relatively large expense that faces urban workers in travelling to work, not to speak of the time lost and the inconvenience involved. His children ride to school in taxis paid for by the local authority. He lives in an environment which is often beautiful and tranquil, and in reach of villages where an active social life may be enjoyed. With his motor car, he is as mobile as any town worker, and the same range of amusements is open to him. Those which involve out-of-door pursuits, such as football, cricket, sailing, fishing and country walking, are even more accessible than they would be to a town worker.

All this is a far cry from the position even twenty years ago, and very certainly from that which obtained before the last war, when many farm families rarely, if ever, left their valleys and the outside world was a strange and somewhat frightening place to them. That things have improved tremendously compared to the life of townsmen is shown by the fact that, despite the continual reduction through mechanisation in the number of those working on the land, there is more than a trickle of men who leave their jobs in town to come and work in the country.

Are farming people happier than they were twenty years ago now that they are, materially speaking, so much better off? This is a subjective question that is not easy to answer. I think that apart from the accident of ill-health, injury, and personal temperament, which applies to everyone at all times and in all regions and classes, the answer may be found in the simple enquiry: 'Are they happily married?' Twenty years ago divorce was still fairly infrequent in the countryside, although whether this necessarily implied that married people living together were invariably happy is not something about which one can pontificate. They presumably made the best of the situation and as a result might have made, for the most part, happier marriages and homes for their children. Nowadays, with the motor car at their disposal, it is all too tempting to venture out and see if the grass on the other side of the hill is greener, and it all too often seems to be so. And with the examples of other ways of life offered by television every evening, there is less and less inhibition about searching for them. The result is the widespread incidence of divorce, broken homes, family misery and instability. The Welfare State seems almost to encourage the process by the facilities it offers to a departing spouse if it is the wife who deserts her husband. The local authority will immediately put her at the top of the housing queue and her needs will be taken care of by supplementary benefit, rent and rate rebates and all the other benefits that the State can provide to a person who is deemed to be destitute.

We now have fifty people working full- or part-time at Ashley Chase, of whom twenty-two are married men. In one month of 1985 the wives of four left, either taking the children or going off on their own. We lost an excellent fitter on that occasion because he had to stop work and stay at home to look after his three children to prevent them from being taken into care.

In general terms, the answer to the question whether or not farmworkers are relatively better off now than twenty years ago must be that they certainly are, provided they are contented and stable in their family lives, a condition that luckily still applies to roughly three out of four families.

I think that the quality of village life has declined in the same period partly because, in any village, the percentage of houses occupied by people employed in farming has shrunk. Villages may have increased in size and the quality of houses greatly improved, but the occupants are more and more retired people from town, or people who work in clerical jobs in a neighbouring town and are disassociated from the life of the countryside. There is not too much mixing between the country people and those who have come to live in their midst, and certainly the range of skills required in farming, which was once abundantly available in the villages, has diminished. It is also true that as fewer and fewer houses in the villages are occupied by agricultural workers, the farmer has had to assume a greater burden for supplying the housing which his work-force will have to occupy if they are to do the work.

The impact of law on the relations of the farmer to his employees is considerable. Annual wage awards underpin the wage structure, and an elaborate code regulates safety at work. To this there can be no reasonable objection. However, several changes over the last decade or so have taken place in the law regarding employment, with ludicrously unjust effects.

One of them relates to tied cottages. There are many types of employment where the occupation of living quarters is deemed to go with the job and where the employee expects to give up possession of his home when he loses his employment. This applies in the cases of the Prime Minister, the police, school teachers in boarding schools, soldiers, sailors and airmen, and a host of other occupations. It is also even true of farming. How could a farmer, whose farm was situated miles from any town or even village, expect to hire farm labour unless he could offer a house on his farm in which the farmworker could live? Would he not also expect in the case of a stock-farm or dairy to have his farmworker live near the buildings housing the herd at night, in case of emergency? A cow might have a difficult calving, a fire might start, flooding might occur, even cattle-rustling is a potential hazard in some districts.

Although the farmworker would normally have had six months' security of tenure, this did not apply where efficient farm management would be seriously prejudiced if the cottage were not available to another worker. That was how matters stood before the Rent (Agriculture) Act 1976, or the Tied Cottage Bill, as it was familiarly called in its passage through Parliament. There were approximately 135,000 farm cottages, of which 70,000 on 35,000 farms were occupied by 50 per cent of all full-time agricultural workers, and 7,000 by their surviving dependants. Prior to the Act, 77 per cent of all cowmen were in tied cottages.

The National Union of Agricultural and Allied Workers in 1906 had called for the abolition of the agricultural tied cottage and, as a result, every Labour Party manifesto since 1945 had undertaken to abolish the tied-cottage system, despite the fact that opinion among farmworkers had completely changed. Prior to the 1976 Act less than 50 per cent of all farmworkers were members of the Union of Agricultural and Allied Workers, and neither union nor non-union members wanted the abolition of tied cottages. In fact one poll found that barely 5 per cent of farmworkers wanted it, and that about 83 per cent felt that the existing system had some advantages for them. So this new piece of legislation, which was capable of doing so much harm to farmers, was enacted not to satisfy any body of opinion among farmers or farmworkers in 1976, but to keep faith with the demand of a farmworkers' union in 1906!

I was doubly interested in the progress of the debate, not merely because I then had about twenty houses whose occupation was about to be regulated by the Bill's provisions, but because my former law partner, Hugh Rossi, MP, as he then was, was the chief assistant to Francis Pym, MP, in resisting its progress through the committee stage of the House of Commons. He had little farming knowledge and my supply of information on the practical consequences of this Bill was therefore of some use to him. I followed the debate in *Hansard* with great keenness. The contributions from Francis Pym, who is a farmer, were pertinent and incisive. One or two of the Liberals were knowledgeable and fair-minded, but the conduct of most of the Labour members of the committee was perfectly appalling. Some even appeared to be guided by dislike of the farmer, but most simply voted according to the party line, apparently regardless of the arguments. If this is a typical case of how our legislature makes law, and it probably is, one need go no further in attributing the blame for so much of the wrong-headed and utterly useless nature of the increasingly multitudinous laws which govern us.

The provisions of the Act simply converted what was a licence to occupy a house by reason of one's occupation into a regulated tenancy under the Rent Act 1968, and extended the right to the farmworker's spouse or other member of his family living with him during the previous six months. It omitted the Crown, local authorities, new towns and housing corporations from its provisions, so that it was pretty obviously a class-motivated piece of legislation aimed at private farmers. The more canny Scots ensured that the Act would not apply to them.

So the farmworker obtained a lifetime tenancy unless the farmer could prove to an Agricultural Dwelling-House Advisory Committee that it was in the interest of efficient agriculture for a new farmworker to be housed in the accommodation, and if it was, it was then up to the Local Housing Authority to use their best endeavours to rehouse the dismissed farmworker.

To operate smoothly, the Act obviously required a local authority which was not unfriendly to the farming interest, and which also had an adequate stock of housing. Its operation must have been horrific to farmers who happened to live under a Labour-controlled authority with anti-farming proclivities.

At first the Act seemed to work pretty well in Dorset. There was a supply of houses recently vacated at the Piddlehinton Camp, and the local authority was favourably disposed towards the farming interest. But when the houses in this former Army camp filled up, conditions became more difficult and the senseless nature of this legislation became manifest. It became commonplace for a former employee to take a job in a town miles away or with another farmer while continuing to live in the house that was required for his successor. It was as if a defeated Prime Minister insisted on staying in Downing Street after he had become Leader of the Opposition. There were cases where caravans had to be brought in to house the new men who were urgently needed to milk the cows or tend the stock, while the former employees actually drove to and from their new employment, or to collect their dole money and social security benefits, before returning to the houses from which they could not be moved.

It became necessary for me on one occasion to give notice to an employee, with whose work I was seriously dissatisfied. He thereupon told us that he would stay in his house until he had found another job carrying with it another house. At that time it was taking four months for the Local Authority Housing Committee to provide alternative accommodation. Even when they were able to offer another house, if the former employee refused to leave, their only remedy was to apply to the County Court, which could well take a further two months.

In another case a man who occupied one of our houses was given notice for what we regarded as perfectly good reasons. When he was offered alternative accommodation by the Housing Authority, however, he said that he wanted to live in Dorchester because that was where he could get a job. Some time after, when he was offered a house in Dorchester, he refused it because he then wanted to live in a particular village for family reasons. At one time I began to think that nothing less than a country manor

would satisfy him and wondered whether the Housing Committee had such accommodation available. It was nineteen months
before I secured possession of my property, during which time the
man continued to live at my, and the taxpayers', expense.

An army of social welfare officers exists to look after people,
many of whom are capable of looking after themselves, but who
are encouraged not to do so by the facilities and resources made
available to them by the public authorities. If one complains about
injustice to the Ministry or the Local Authority, or even to the
National Farmers Union, one gets a prompt brush off. A system
looks reasonable on paper, so they assume it is so in practice. Why
should they involve themselves in the thorny world of practical
facts; and where, so often, would their own jobs be if matters
were arranged more sensibly? The extraordinary complacency of
the NFU in the face of my complaints about the working of this
Act was one of the reasons that prompted me to terminate my
membership of that organization. If facts cut no ice for them in
comparison with theory, then I reckoned that their local branch
could face with equanimity another fact, which was the loss of my
£1,000-a-year subscription.

Another example of ludicrous law is that dealing with what is
called 'wrongful dismissal'. It was enacted in the Employment
Protection Act that any employee who was dismissed without
good cause shown in writing, and before having received two
previous warnings in writing in the case of transgression, was
entitled to damages for wrongful dismissal against his employer, if
he could prove that his dismissal was not in the form provided for
in the Act. We had a wonderful example of what that could mean.

We felt compelled to dismiss a particular employee, not for any
misconduct but because we were not pleased with the quality of
his work. He brought an action against us for wrongful dismissal

on the grounds that he had not had two written warnings before the final dismissal. The case was heard before a Tribunal of three people, one representing the worker's interest, another the employer's, and the third who was supposedly neutral. I had to pay a solicitor and hire counsel. The hearing took nearly two days. All three members of the Tribunal decided in my favour which, however, did not mean that I could recover my costs, which amounted to about £2,000. The loser in most actions usually has party-and-party costs awarded against him, which acts as a disincentive against frivolous litigation, but not in cases of wrongful dismissal. Up and down the country in factories, offices and farms, this action is open to dismissed employees who can obtain Legal Aid and who rarely have to pay any costs, even when they lose their actions. It is almost an incentive to blackmail and is certainly a disincentive to employment.

A third instance of absurd and unjust law has not affected me but is an increasing factor in changing the ownership of farms and breaking up good farming businesses. Before the Matrimonial Causes Act of 1973 and subsequent legislation, the financial settlement received after a divorce or separation depended on the guilt or innocence of the parties in respect of what was regarded as a matrimonial offence. The settlement then made by the Court related to income and not capital, so that in the case of a farmer found guilty of committing a matrimonial offence for which a decree of divorce had been obtained by his wife, his ability to farm his land and to pass ownership on to his children was not affected, even though his enjoyment deriving from the profits of it was lessened. The Act of 1973 changed all that. It pilloried the idea of divorce through the committal of a matrimonial offence and departed from the concept of guilt and innocence, substituting for it the concept of matrimonial breakdown. It also allowed a Court to make awards of capital as well as income.

Tied Cottages and Taxes

I am aware from personal experience how duplicity, skill and falsehood from obscure pressure groups are able to secure great changes in the law without the general public realising what has been accomplished to their detriment for some considerable time afterwards. The way this particular law can operate was shown by an unfortunate incident in the Bride Valley a few years ago. A farmer from Hampshire bought a 150-acre holding not far from us and almost immediately had the great misfortune to contract meningitis. He recovered, but being unable to run his farm unaided, he took on a farmworker who formed an attachment with the farmer's wife. A divorce ensued and the farmer not only lost his wife but his farm too.

One can see that matrimonial law has parted from any concept of justice. It would be difficult to convince many practising lawyers of the lack of justice in the current matrimonial law because the profit to them in assisting in the break-up of a prosperous farm, or any other business, with a scale of costs which is commensurate with the value of the property that is disposed of, must be considerable. We should remember that it was not the legal profession that secured the repeal of laws which provided the death penalty for stealing a sheep or goods to the value of five shillings but merely the propensity of juries to refuse to convict. One recalls that lawyers have in general always been on the side of authority, and when that position redounds to their profit, they are apt to forget that law without justice is merely licensed brigandage.

With divorce now claiming one-third of all marriages, the provisions of the Matrimonial Causes Act 1973 are likely to result in the sale of an increasing number of farms and deprive increasing numbers of farmers' children of their chance of inheriting farms from their parents, and for no other reason than the imbecility of our legislature and its inability to understand elementary concepts of justice.

Finally, one comes to the subject of capital taxes, which are simply the means of depriving children of the right to inherit from their parents. There are two forms, Capital Gains Tax and Inheritance Tax. At the time of writing, the first deprives a person of anything up to one-third of his property, should he wish to sell his farm or another asset or give it to his children, even though the alleged gain is nothing more than a paper one made as a result of government having debased the currency. The second is a tax of up to 60 per cent on a farm or asset passing from parents to children. Even if such a tax is subject to the lesser rates applicable in the case of farming assets, it virtually ensures the break-up of a family business. At the very best, it puts an end to improvements and efficiency, since most of the profits then go for many years to pay the tax. These capital taxes have proved a major factor in the collapse of British industry and the increasing domination of the country by foreign business interests. They are part of that system of state brigandage which has so devastated our industry and commerce and made of us a third-rate country within two generations.

CHAPTER *10*

To Enjoy, to Work, and to Defend

We talk of owning land, and the concept of a freehold certainly includes the idea of perpetual ownership. How we, who ourselves have only a short tenure to life, imagine that we 'own' land that has been there in the same recognizable form for hundreds or thousands of years before we were born, and will be there for just as long after we have been put under it, is difficult to fathom. It is best to consider it as one of those legal fictions which enable us to go about our business in a sensible way without our having to consider the deeper philosophical truth of the relationship.

Ownership of such a commodity as land, which from a human point of view is virtually eternal, really means its temporary custody. It allows us, within limits, to deface or beautify it, neglect it or make it fruitful. We are in a position of responsibility towards it and it has the power to inspire us with love for it.

Before I acquired a new farm I would walk over it with John, usually with a spade, so as to gauge the depth of the soil and its composition. After its purchase we would walk over every field again, surveying every copse, hedge and hollow, so as to decide the best use to put it to. The object was to bring as much of it as possible to the highest point of fertility. This often involved clearing it of weeds, improving its drainage, redirecting water channels, demolishing unnecessary hedges, removing dead trees, re-seeding, liming and manuring and, of course, building both barns and dairies.

But I never felt that any newly acquired field was really mine until I had actually done some physical work on it. This would take place in Summer during harvest time. On those fields marked out for silaging, we would, some time in August, after the grass had been cut for silage, cut once more for hay, which would be baled and then left in the fields in so many rectangular bales ready for stacking, before being carted off to the hay-barns. In those fields where corn was grown, straw would be baled and left in the same way. I made it my self-appointed task to make some of those stacks of seventeen, with five on the bottom, four on the second layer, four on the third and four on the top. Sometimes the bales would be light and dry and weigh not more than 25 or 30 lbs each, and sometimes the hay or straw would be wet and heavy and the bales would weigh up to 70 lbs each. I would strip to the waist and get down to the task in the heat of the day. My hands would be calloused from tugging at the twine while sweat would pour off me as I went through a field building up my stacks. Roby would sometimes come and help me and Cedric too when he was small, and if I was working on a hillside, they would roll the bales down the hill towards me. I became aware of every contour of that field, and when I stopped for a while either to give my hands a rest, or to let the baler catch up with me and deposit a few more bales in the field, I would see what lay about me, often from a previously unremarked spot.

Sometimes I found myself near the heavy green foliage of a nearby woodland, and sometimes in a remote corner of the estate

The revenue hut on Puncknowle Knoll built to deter smuggling, but later used to spot mackerel shoals

Bim Wrixon with his favourite cow, Hearty

Charley Miller outside his cottage

on which I had hardly been before. And sometimes when we were baling on Tenants Hill or the flank of Abbotsbury Hill, I could see the sun shining on the sea, laying down what seemed to be a glittering path across it to the shores of Devon. I discovered that outdoor labour and exercise is one of the greatest pleasures given to man and that contrary to the beliefs of town-bred scholars and people who work in offices, the labouring countrymen who, until recently, formed the greater part of the population of most countries, were probably the happiest part of mankind so long as they kept their health and vigour. At such times I really felt I owned that field and had an understanding of what I needed to do to smooth out its deficiencies or unsightliness, to improve and bring it to fruitfulness.

Sometimes Colette would come out with me and sit on a bale while she served tea. Always Ginnie would be there, scampering about, chasing hares and rabbits and then, panting with the fatigue of the chase, lying by us on the grass, tired and happy.

I have not until now said a word about Ginnie, but for ten years she was an almost indispensable part of our lives. The boys had always wanted to have a dog and the desire strengthened when we acquired Ashley Chase, for here surely was the ideal place to romp about with one. One day in 1971 John rang me up to ask if the boys still wanted a dog, 'for I think I have got one that might suit them.' The doubt sprang from uncertainty as to whether or not the poor animal was still alive: for it belonged to one of our dairymen, but as it had developed a propensity for his chickens, its fate was at that moment in the balance. Luckily it had not been shot or otherwise disposed of and the next day John brought it to us. She was a mongrel collie crossed with a Jack Russell, the fruit of an adventure of John's Jack Russell, Judy, with Dr Dewhurst's collie. She was black and white and looked like a small collie. The only traces of a Jack Russell in her were her short legs and her hunting instincts.

It was our first dog and the boys were delighted with her. I, simply foreseeing trouble, insisted that the animal would have to sleep outside the house. That night there was whining, howling and barking, and soon I was being told by Colette and the boys that the poor animal could not be left out in the cold and the dark, but should be allowed into the house. I gave way but stipulated that she must be confined to the scullery. I do not know quite how it happened, but within three days Ginnie had managed to convince us that her night quarters was our bedroom. Within a week she had gone a step further. She waited until the lights were out and then in a single bound jumped onto the foot of our bed and there went to sleep. That was her bed for the rest of her life and once she had trained us to accept it, it never occurred to us that she should sleep anywhere else.

Although Ginnie had come to us on the understanding that she was to be the 'boys' dog', she herself decided that, apart from mealtimes when she would make a beeline for Colette, I was to be her companion-in-chief. From the moment I emerged dressed for breakfast, she was tailing me. The big moment for her was the walk. She used to wait for me under the table while I had breakfast, and grew steadily more impatient if I lingered over it. Finally she got me out of the house and she was then in her element.

It is not unusual for a townsman, once he has acquired a country estate, to develop a strong taste for what are seen as the country sports, particularly hunting, shooting and fishing. In fact, the ability to follow such pursuits is supposedly one of the many inducements to own land. Sporting activity was not however one of the things I had in mind when buying Ashley Chase. I had ridden occasionally and fished from time to time, but had done neither seriously, and owning a great tract of land did not change me in this respect. A stock-farm necessitates a great many fences, which rather precludes horse-riding. I did not ride well enough to hunt, though I have no objection to fox-hunting, but shooting herbivorous animals was something I had never done, and never intended to do. The idea of shooting a beautiful unsuspecting creature, simply because it moves and provides an interesting target, appals me, whether it be deer, hare, rabbit, partridge or pheasant. This objection to shooting that part of the animal creation which does me no harm and which I do not require for food does not carry over to humans. There have been in this century whole categories of those whom I would have thought it a public duty to despatch.

The 150 acres or so of woods at Ashley Chase harboured at least fifty head of roe deer. As I did not shoot them, and did my best to prevent others from doing so, their number sharply increased when the shooting season started on the neighbouring Abbotsbury and Puncknowle estates. The same went for pheasants, partridges, woodcock and buzzards.

What I loved to do was to go out with Ginnie and wander for hours on the Downs and on the remote combes as well as in the woods of Ashley Chase, almost regardless of the weather or of time. Obviously it was best in the sunshine when the brilliant light invested every feature of land and sky with colour and a luminous quality that filled me with joy and awe. But I also used to walk off, with Ginnie at my heels, under a grey sky, when it rained, even in the thick mists that swept in from the sea. I have been completely lost in thick fog atop our Downs, hardly able to make out my feet until I came upon a hollow, a copse or a wire fence which gave me a clue to where I was.

ASHLEY CHASE: *A Dorset Domain*

In such conditions, the deer I found grazing in the fields or browsing in the woods, or the hare springing up from its cover nearby, or the pheasant suddenly erupting from a thicket, were more like companions than quarries to be hunted. Of course Ginnie used to give chase, sometimes coursing over two or three fields in pursuit, but she never caught anything. So she and I hunted without bloodshed or harm done. I often came across a couple of deer which suddenly rose from the ground and gracefully took a wire fence or hedge. So we would return home, I having seen memorable sights and also having noted the conditions of the pastures, the fences, the drainage, the woodlands and hedges, and the state of buildings; while Ginnie would be covered in mud, exhausted by the exertions of the chase, but deeply contented, to lie down by the fire and to turn from a beast of the chase to a tame and loving house pet.

When it grew too hot I would retire to our garden. This had gradually grown from about two to nearly seven acres. There was no regularity about it, and therein lay a good deal of its beauty and charm. We had built a tennis court and a swimming pool. We had planted lines of different pines as a windbreak to the south-west of the house, which to our surprise made an enclosed walk 100 yards long and sheltered from wherever the winds blew. Beyond it, on rising ground, we planted another two acres with Monterey cypress, larch and Corsica pines, not knowing which would do best on that wind-swept ground. We hoped that eventually they would all do well. To the south, finding that the part of the field which lay outside the garden was permanently water-logged owing to greensand, we annexed an acre of it to the garden and planted it with poplar, partly to mop up the water and partly for the pleasure of watching the delicately turned leaves rustle in the breeze. Flowerbeds and ornamental trees were planted here and there with the result that the garden, which originally was a bare hillside, acquired the characteristics of an enclosed paradise. Set in the midst of rolling hills and combes, which had been turned into a great milk-producing enterprise, and which at times were combed by tractors and trailers, dung-spreaders and harvesters, it was an oasis of peace and tranquillity.

It had its own movement related to the seasons, and to watch it was like listening to a great symphony which lasted throughout the year and unfolded in colours and the development of trees, shrubs and flowers. It began in February with the snowdrops finding their way through frozen-hard soil. These were succeeded by delicate little crocuses which were soon followed by daffodils tentatively putting up their shoots, often through a carpet of snow, only waiting for the sun to shine and the earth to grow warm before sending forth their countless yellow flowers in great masses of glorious colour. Then the delicate cherry blossoms would flower in thick clumps of pink and white, and just as they were getting to look their best, the azalea, rhododendron and camellia would start to flower in majestic purple, white and red; while in May, the great Davidia involucrata, our Chinese Hand-kerchief tree, would put out its white leaves and the clematis and wistaria would climb over the house and walls. Meanwhile, all about us the different indigenous trees, chestnut, willow, poplar, alder, ash and oak, would be fanning out their leaves of fresh light green, giving a wondrous mix of light, shade and protection to the more exotic trees and shrubs.

By July everything was green but for the hydrangeas, some early dahlias and banks of roses we had introduced to the garden. Then the majestic golds, yellows and russets of Autumn would end the year until they themselves gave way to the delicate leafless branches of trees in Winter, brightened sometimes by frost and snow and prefacing the renewal of that year-long symphony of nature once more. In mid-Summer we would swim under our great Corsican pines, with the reflection of the pavilion in the water of the pool. Under the burning sun we could easily imagine ourselves on some Mediterranean isle without the crowds, the humidity and the pollution. In this little Eden, this Demi-Paradise, we would swim, play tennis, walk or read. This was the deeply happy and tranquil centre of all the busy activity round about us.

The Bride Valley, and the even more remote valleys and hills which slope into it, seems to have been spared most of the stirring events that form the staple of history. Luckily for its inhabitants, no famous battle was fought on its gentle terrain since the time of the Romans, and no cruel massacres were perpetrated in the name of religion or ideas of government. Just as luckily for its unmarred beauty, no great mineral deposits were discovered on it and no great manufacturing centre developed in it. The fact that the adjacent coastline does not consist of a sheltered sandy shore, like that of Bournemouth forty miles to the east, but is lined by the steeply shelving pebbles of the Chesil Beach, and that Lyme Bay is open to the full force of the gales and surges of the Atlantic and is full of dangerous currents capable of drowning a person swimming or boating only a few yards from the shore, has contributed also to the situation that, apart from the little village of West Bexington, there is no coastal resort between Weymouth and Bridport.

Yet it is clear from the multitude of barrows, those burial sites of the Ancient Britons, that this valley was not always an isolated backwater. For the pre-Celtic population, these hill pastures must have been one of the most thickly populated regions of settlement in this island. The place of worship which they built on Tenants Hill, now known as the Kingston Russell Stone Circle, shows that for centuries it was a place of sanctity for the inhabitants of the area. Only eight miles to the east lies Maiden Castle, the greatest Iron Age fortification in Britain. Built as a place of refuge by the Durotriges, the ruling Celtic tribe of Dorset in the first century, it was stormed by the Romans with much bloodshed. Abbotsbury Castle, a small but similar earthwork, lies atop the hill which separates the Bride Valley from the sea. From its 700 foot height, in good weather, the whole of Lyme Bay can be seen. The Romans placed a garrison there to look out for incursions from the sea, so that, for all we know, the valley may have been the scene of violent action 2,000 years ago; but in the Middle Ages a calm seems to have descended upon it, punctuated only by the great catastrophe of the Black Death which had the same devastating effect here as in other parts of England.

While the great Benedictine Abbey of Abbotsbury owned much of it, the valley of Ashley and Gorwell seems to have belonged to a monastic cell established by the Carthusian Abbey of Netley in Hampshire. St Luke's Chapel in what is now Chapel Wood, dating from the fourteenth century, may have been built by them, and they themselves presumably led lives of prayer and silent meditation in the woods and adjacent hills which lend themselves even now, and must have done so even more then, to thoughts of God and His creation.

With the coming of the Reformation, the Bride Valley, without being drawn into the centre of events, sometimes stood only just outside them. In 1539 the great Abbey of Abbotsbury was secularised and demolished, its lands sold to the Fox-Strangways family, who still own most of them today. In 1588 the Spanish Armada could have been descried from Abbotsbury Hill as it made its way just two miles offshore out of the treacherous bay and rounded Portland Bill. In 1644 there was one sharp skirmish at

Abbotsbury between Royalists coming up from Bridport and a Parliamentary group under Lord Ashley Cooper coming from Salisbury, culminating in the destruction of much of both forces when the Fox-Strangways's house, which had been used to store ammunition by the Parliamentary forces, blew up. In 1685 a look-out on Abbotsbury Hill could have seen the ships of the Duke of Monmouth's little fleet making for Lyme during his ill-fated rebellion, while three years later, a little further out to sea, the large Dutch fleet of William of Orange could have been seen sailing for Torbay to initiate the 'Glorious Revolution'.

Then silence and obscurity descended on the valley. A few houses for gentlemen were built and a few villages were established but nothing happened to change the essential character of a valley, enclosed on three sides by hills, whose dominant features were its rural seclusion and the introverted life of its people. Even the founding of the Bridehead Estate at the eastern end of the valley by the Williams family at the beginning of the nineteenth century did not materially change the picture. Rural poverty, punctuated occasionally by illicit windfalls from the gains of smuggling on the nearby coast, must have been the lot of most in a wholly subsistence economy. Even Thomas Hardy, who illumined the life of so much of early nineteenth-century Dorset, chose to ignore the Bride Valley. Abbotsbury is mentioned under the name 'Abbotsea', and Bridport under 'Port-Bredy', as is Portesham where Admiral Hardy lived, but not the valley itself or its villages. But this obscurity, this air of being forgotten by the onward rush of change and modernity, was not the least of the things that sometimes made me aware, as I wandered on its hills and dales, of those sparks of the Divine creation which permeate our world.

These days, however, the price exacted from those concerned to preserve the beauty and harmony of town, or village, or stretch of countryside, is ever-watchful vigilance. The fact that a particular area may be designated by government as of 'outstanding natural beauty' certainly means that any farmer who wishes to put up a barn or a house has to run the gauntlet of County Land Agents, Planning Officers and Planning Committees. The system offers, however, no protection from the greatest danger of modern times, the State. Its regulations simply do not apply to the Crown or to Crown-appointed institutions.

The reader will have seen how ineffective these regulations were to restrain the Forestry Commission from devastating our valley with a clear fell of 100 acres of our woodland, and its replacement by a massive belt of conifers. Two other instances of gross nuisance came to assail the quiet and beauty of the Bride Valley during my occupation of Ashley Chase.

The first came from the most unexpected quarter, the sky. My house is about ten miles north-west of the naval helicopter base on Portland, HMS *Osprey*. From there helicopter pilots are trained in flights over Lyme Bay and the coastline. One day in 1968 we discovered that Lady Williams had leased about fifteen acres of her side of Tenants Hill to the Royal Navy for a helicopter landing-base. It was just east of our own eastern boundary with the Bridehead estate. Had the pilots confined their flights to the sky over the uninhabited hills, who would have minded these brave and skilful young men learning to fly the machines which have proved so useful in war and peace? Unfortunately for us, they decided to use our house as a marker, and we were suddenly aware of their presence on certain days of the week in an excruciating way. They formed the habit of circling our house at a height of only a few hundred feet for minutes at a time, and when one helicopter finished its stint, another would take over, and the whole day would be shattered by the tremendous noise made by relays of these infernal hornets as, after a while, we began to call them.

I complained to the Commander of HMS Osprey without much luck. His men, he said, had instructions to keep above 1,000 feet and it was unthinkable, he felt, that they should disobey orders; I must be mistaken in my assumption that they were flying round and round my house. Others defended the practice by saying it was in the national interest to train helicopter pilots and therefore it was a patriotic duty to put up with the noise. But it was not over the houses of these stern patriots that these helicopters were operating. I asked for a public inquiry and one was held in Dorchester under the joint auspices of the Royal Navy and the West Dorset Planning Committee. I quoted my evidence and a fair hearing was afforded me. My chief witness was General Bond, Lady Williams's own brother and Vice-Chairman of the County Council, a most able man and very incisive in speech.

My main argument to prevent this continuing nuisance was that while I recognized the necessity for Royal Navy helicopter pilots to train over land as well as over water, I saw no reason for them to pick a spot to do it which was right over my house, when by going ten miles north-east of their base instead of the same distance north-west, they would find themselves in similar countryside but without the possibility of annoying anyone. In short, why not fly over the tank-training area round Bovington, where they could make as much noise as they liked since it would be lost in the noise-making activities which went on there all week? The answer came that Bovington was under the control of the Army. The Navy had asked for permission to use the skies above this tank-training area and had been refused. 'What rank did the officer in charge of Bovington hold?' asked General Bond.

'Brigadier,' came the reply. 'Did you not ask him a second time?' asked Bond with some severity. 'You could have done that, or appealed over his head.' 'We did not, I am afraid,' said the Navy officer somewhat meekly. 'But you will now, won't you?' said General Bond, and the request was echoed by the Planning Officer. They did, and this time their request was granted. A compromise was agreed: two of the training helicopters would fly over Bovington and the other two would keep to the Bride Valley, but would try to avoid hunting us round our garden.

The second nuisance was far more menacing. One day Eddie Fry told me that there was a proposal by the Central Electricity Generating Board to build a nuclear power station on the Chesil Beach. I could hardly believe my ears. It was, however, true enough. The CEGB was proposing to put up a water-cooled nuclear power station in the middle of one of the loveliest sections of unspoilt coastline in Britain. Nor was it to be a modest affair; it would measure 500 feet in length, 250 in width and would be 250 feet high. Eddie mentioned that a retired Army man, a Major Griffith, who lived in the village of Langton Herring in the very shadow of where this monstrous construction was to be sited, was the organizer of local opposition to the scheme and had already collected 20,000 signatures of local residents against the proposal. I invited him over to explain the proposal and the objections to it, and Colette and I, with Admiral Sir John Hamilton, who lived in Abbotsbury and had expressed a desire to be present, listened in rapt attention to the account we were given of this horrific proposal. Major Griffith then let me have newspaper clippings and the record of a Parliamentary Committee which gave the details of the proposal.

The Central Electricity Generating Board had decided back in the 1970s that Britain was going to need far more power for industry, transport and the home by the end of the century than it then used, and that the fossil fuels, coal, oil and gas, would be entirely inadequate to supply the demand. The only means of coping with this enormous increase in demand would, in their view, be by nuclear energy. They had therefore drawn up a plan to provide water-cooled nuclear reactors every thirty miles along Britain's coastline.

Their method of reasoning was curious, and exhibited every sign of having been devised to meet a pre-ordained conclusion. It was deemed axiomatic that Britain's need for power would increase by a certain percentage every year, although in fact it never did. It was also stated, without argument, that no other suitable fuel was available because, in their words, North Sea oil was too far away to be utilised, as was coal from the Midlands. It ignored the proximity of the South Wales coalfield and the fact that the English Channel and the chalk hills near it were even then considered to have large-scale reserves of both gas and oil.

The CEGB, having decided that this chain of nuclear-fuel reactors was necessary, further decided on grounds which seemed somewhat irrational that water-cooled reactors were the best for its purpose. It was a curious decision, not merely on the grounds of safety but also of cost. As regards safety, the water-cooled reactor at Three Mile Island in New Jersey had just been closed down as a result of nuclear-fuel leaks. Of the three types of nuclear-fuel reactor in operation, the gas-cooled one perfected in Canada and called CANDU was by far the cheapest to build and was the one most commonly used. France, then the biggest user of nuclear energy in Europe, relying on nuclear power for 60 per cent of its energy, had built only these. No satisfactory reason was given in the CEGB report for rejecting this type of nuclear station, which had a far greater safety record and was far cheaper to build.

On the question of cost, the CEGB had estimated that each of these water-cooled nuclear reactors would cost the country no more than £1.4 billion, for this was the cost of each of five identical nuclear stations that had been started in the State of Washington in the United States. What it omitted to point out was that work on these stations had come to a halt as it became clear, after work had started, that the project would cost four times the amount estimated. The mind boggled at what the English water-cooled nuclear power stations would cost, and it seemed that the erection of these huge and potentially dangerous structures was well beyond the nation's requirement and its resources.

The House of Commons Select Committee, which examined the project and heard expert evidence of every kind, came to the conclusion that the CEGB had shown both incompetence and mendacity in preparing and issuing its proposals, and that the power-supply companies which had given their advice to it had been activated by greed. Its detailed conclusions, which would have spelt bankruptcy to any non-government controlled body, were quite startling in their condemnation of both the CEGB and its advisers.

They started off by saying that 'It would have been less misleading and more helpful to the Committee if the CEGB had informed us during their first evidence session that the forecasts contained in their memorandum had already been overtaken by events and were in the process of being revised downwards . . . having examined the economic case for the policy announced by the Secretary of State and in particular the figures supplied by the CEGB, we have concluded that many of the underlying assumptions are open to question and that the justification for a steady ordering programme of 15 GW over ten years rests on premises which are necessarily very uncertain', and went on to conclude that 'We would have greater confidence in the Board's argument if we were convinced that it addressed itself as vigorously to the economic case for investing in a programme at all, as it does to the relative merits of coal and nuclear', and that in sum 'the net effective cost figures produced by the Board are difficult to follow, inadequately presented, and based on questionable and often unspecified assumptions. It would have been in our view far more helpful to an objective appraisal of the economic case for the 15 GW programme if the CEGB had provided for each new station the estimated construction and unit generating cost together with the underlying assumptions and range of uncertainties.'

On the question of which nuclear reactor to use, the House of Commons Committee was equally scathing. 'It is clear to us,' they said, 'that the CANDU reactor has not been seriously considered by the Government or any of its advisory bodies since 1974 . . . It seems to us that having burnt their fingers with a heavy-water reactor type, considerably different from CANDU, and which in any case is generally admitted to have been of a very poor design, the Government and industry have turned away from this concept. All this is astonishing in the light of CANDU's excellent performance and properties, described in evidence by Lord Bowden. We do not,' they went on, 'believe that CANDU's excellent record can be challenged. We regret that there has been a failure to examine CANDU seriously at a stage in its development when its merits should have been fully and fairly assessed . . .' The Committee concluded 'that enormous past nuclear investments have had exceptionally low productivity, great resources have been used with very little direct return and serious net loss.'

These devastating criticisms, which would have been enough to scupper any private company, did not seem to deter the CEGB, however, and they were planning to come to a decision as to the best spot in Britain to build the first of this new generation of nuclear-generating plants. The choice was between Hinckley Point on the Somerset coast, where two nuclear-fuel plants already existed, Plymouth and Herbury Bay. Where the devil, one might have asked, was Herbury Bay? I had never heard of it, and yet it seemed that it was only six miles or so from my estate. I pored over a local map and eventually found it. It was not in any standard guide of Dorset, nor in the Yachting Map of the Coast, nor in the 1 inch-to-the-mile detailed Ordnance Survey. It turned out to be no bay facing the sea, but a shallow indentation of the mainland, no more than 300 yards wide at its mouth, on the brackish waters of the Fleet, a lagoon lying between the Chesil Bank and the mainland. It had about as much geographical significance as my 'nine-acre wood' or my 'twelve-acre Pink Lake coppice'. The denomination of a vast nuclear-fuel plant under the unknown name of Herbury Bay would convey nothing as to its real whereabouts to anyone in the Kingdom, save for a few inquisitive men who lived in one of the two or three villages bordering the Fleet, and in that name lay another example of the duplicity so strikingly unmasked by the House of Commons Select Committee. For had the CEGB given out its intention to build one of its vast and potentially dangerous nuclear-fuel stations on the Fleet, or on the Chesil Bank, it would instantly have attracted the attention of tens of thousands of people who had spent their holidays in or round the delightful coast from Weymouth to Bridport, or driven along that coast road with its sublime views of the Chesil Beach and Portland to the east, and Golden Cap and the cliffs of West Dorset and East Devon to the west. Nature lovers, conservationists and ordinary people everywhere would have abhorred the wanton spoliation of our countryside and coasts, and would have been up in arms at this outrageous act of depredation, and the CEGB would have had as much chance of getting away with this project as if they had tried to erect their nuclear power station in Kew Gardens. But to build at 'Herbury Bay' would have given them a chance to slip by with a decision which could then be defended as an accomplished fact.

Apart from the devastation on the adjacent coastline if the CEGB got their way, I could foresee an accident of the Three Mile Island variety in my vicinity which would lead to an evacuation of Ashley Chase and a cessation of all farming activity. I therefore offered my services to Major Griffith. He had already done all that was humanly possible to acquaint the local community with the project and to rouse them against it. What had not yet been done was to draw the attention of the country at large to what was seemingly intended for this section of the South Coast. I proposed that we hire a well-known film producer and TV commentator to make a half-hour nature-study film on the Chesil Bank and its hinterland and then superimpose on it the massive bulk of the proposed nuclear-fuel power station.

Some initial steps had been taken to carry out this project when an announcement was made that, for the time being at any rate, Hinckley Point had been chosen as the intended site of the first of the new model of nuclear-power station to be built in Britain. Meanwhile the whole issue was to be re-argued in connection with a coastal site at Sizewell in Essex. A decision in that case is awaited. If the CEGB get their way there, I do not think that we have won much more than a temporary reprieve for the Chesil Beach. Nothing is safe from the depredations of the Nation-State these days, and if this harmonious and beautiful countryside is to be preserved, it will be so only by continual vigilance and the will of its people actively to oppose any attempt to despoil it.

CHAPTER *11*

Cheddar and Blue Vinny

To my contentment, our cheese production went from strength to strength for the first six years from 1973. Of course we had our troubles; cheesemakers always do. Milk which most people would consider perfectly clean and acceptable might be quite unfit for cheese. Cattle grazing on kale or even eating a few dandelions in the permanent pastures could have made their milk unfit for cheesemaking. It was necessary to have a complete chain of purity, embracing the pastures on which the cattle grazed, the water they drank, the cleanliness of their dairies, the bulk tankers in which the milk was stored and transported, and the pipes and equipment in the cheese dairy, so as to eliminate the possibility of 'phage', the bane of all cheesemakers. Should a little antibiotic or even colostrum get into the milk in a particular dairy, or the starter develop a weakness, the cheese would develop a 'taint' or 'go dead', and the result would be a down-grading, a forced sale and a loss on that particular production batch; but on the whole we made good Cheddar. Most of it was fine-graded and we began to win commendations and silver cups for our efforts. Production also went up, and by 1979, with 1,000,000 gallons a year of milk going through our cheese dairy, we were making about 450 tons of quality Cheddar annually.

The consumption of cheese in Britain amounts annually to about 300,000 tons. Cheddar forms 68 per cent of this tonnage. When I first started to make Cheddar in 1973, British production accounted for about 55 per cent of this total, some 165,000 tons. When New Zealand imports, which then amounted to 46,000 tons a year, began to be phased out as part of the new Common Market arrangements, it was reasonable to expect that British producers would be able to step in and replace that 15 per cent of the total tonnage consumed in Britain which emanated from New Zealand. But it did not happen that way. Home-made cheese did gradually increase to 70 per cent of total consumption by 1981, but the main replacement of New Zealand Cheddar on the home market came chiefly from Eire, and then from France, Holland and Germany.

The Milk Marketing Board is a statutory body appointed to take collection of all milk offered for sale in the country. It regulates its price, controls its quality, and decides what production should go to the liquid market, and what should be manufactured and, if the latter, how much should go into making cheese, butter, skim-milk powder and chocolate crumb. In addition to these activities, it also operates through its own company, Dairy Crest, its own cheese and butter-making factories. Its critics have sometimes pointed out that its activities are so various that they can end up defeating the object for which the Board was formed, which was to provide a steady and reasonable marketing structure for the British milk producer. Most of its own production is either of 'mousetrap' quality or, if a bit better than that, a bland, fairly tasteless cheese whose chief virtue is that it is cheap and filling. Most of it does not shed any lustre on the name of Cheddar, and much of it is of such a nondescript taste that it would be better, for the sake of Cheddar's reputation, if it were sold under a different name.

In addition, we have the Ministry of Agriculture whose aim, as far as cheese is concerned, is to encourage the import of indifferent foreign Cheddars at the cheapest price possible so as to keep down the market price. In allowing this, they do not bother to investigate whether or not this imported Cheddar is being dumped here as a result of foreign subsidies. It is one more instance of their concern to keep food prices down regardless of the effect on the home producer.

About 10 per cent of the home production of Cheddar is now produced by the members of the Farmhouse Cheesemakers Association, a loose union of some thirty farmers who operate under a strict system of grading, maturing and joint marketing that ensures that the cheese has reached a level of quality and completed an ageing process, normally at least nine months. That gives it a distinctive Cheddar taste, a good consistency to the touch and an absence of unpleasant odours and flavour. The members of the Farmhouse Cheesemakers Association could easily produce more than 10 per cent but until 1986 the Milk Marketing Board did not allow them to do so. The market usually pays £200 to £500 a ton more for Farmhouse Cheddar than for the milder factory production, and the Board seems to feel that this 9 to 22p a pound extra for a quality production should not be paid on more than 5 per cent of the total amount of cheese consumed in the country. It takes the attitude that cheapness rather than quality should be the dominating characteristic of British food, particularly of cheese; an attitude which has had the backing of British governments for a long time past, and is no doubt a contributory reason for the fact that the people of Britain are deemed to eat worse quality food than the people of any other country in the

Common Market. To obtain this cheap cheese, various curious trading practices are resorted to, including encouraging the importation of three-, four- and five-month old Cheddars from the Continent, which fulfils 40 per cent of British demand, the restriction of cheesemaking in Britain so that the market thus inundated by foreign imports is not 'weakened', and the export of thousands of tons of our own factory-made Cheddar of six weeks of age and less so that it is 'taken out of the market' and does not thereby weaken the price. All this is supposed to help the milk producer and consumer, but a simple man could be forgiven for not quite understanding how it does that.

Once a year the Farmhouse Cheesemakers hold their own exhibition of cheese when they assemble at Shepton Mallet during the annual Royal Bath and West Show. There they lay out in the Cheese Hall the prize-winning cheeses for the delectation of the buyers, the makers, and the trade generally. There, under the great marquee, they lunch with the principal buyers and the representatives of the trade and the press on cold meats and salads, magnificent strawberries with lashings of cream, followed by splendid cheeses, helped down by white and rosé wines. There they award the prizes, hear speeches, and listen to prognostications about the future of the trade. The pleasantness of the occasion depends quite a bit on the weather. It has been known to rain so hard that the water in the marquee has come over the tops of the wellingtons of those who had decided to brave the elements to be there. Once it happened to us that our departure was delayed for two hours as we waited for our car to be pushed out of the field where it was parked by tractors equipped with hay-bales in front of their bonnets to provide cushioning for the impact. But when the weather was favourable these occasions were pleasant and novel. We came into contact with the more successful Somerset businessmen/farmers, the Barbers, Andrew Warren, Richard Longman, Ted Alvis and others who, together with the officials of the Farmhouse Cheesemakers Association such as Stan Thorp and Gordon Walker, had contributed so greatly towards building up the agricultural prosperity of this county from where most of them came. It was at these gatherings that Colette was sometimes called up to receive the cups won by Ashley Chase Cheese Dairies for this or that category of cheese.

It was a pleasant prospect to contemplate the gradual build-up of this new enterprise. Progress, if not spectacular, was steady and I felt I could look forward to a gradual increase in quality production as well as an increase in volume as our milk production gradually rose. Before long it had reached 1,500,000 gallons a year, and by 1983 we were making about 650 tons of Cheddar a year.

Our cheese datum had been raised by 1981 to 1,200,000 gallons per annum for the home market, which meant a cheese production of about 545 tons. If we exceeded that limit, we would face levies. It was odd that these 'fines' were inflicted on an industry which was then only supplying two-thirds of home demand, but those were the rules. There were, however, other cheeses we could manufacture which were outside this limitation, and among them were the so-called 'territorial cheeses', namely cheeses other than Cheddar which were associated with a particular part of the country in which they had, in former times, been made.

The only cheese associated with Dorset in the past was Dorset Blue Vinny, a low-fat blue-veined cheese made from skimmed milk which had previously been made in small quantities by dairymen's wives from surplus milk produced in April and May in the Spring flush. It was called 'the poor man's Stilton' because it had only about 13 per cent fat compared with the 30 to 32 per cent in a good Stilton, and instead of having the rich creamy flavour and texture of the latter, it was dry and crumbly. Its quality varied greatly, depending on who made it. Often it was thought to be fit for only local consumption, but sometimes it graced the cheeseboards of the best London clubs and was more highly thought of than Stilton.

After an effective delivery system for milk had been inaugurated by the Milk Marketing Board in 1937, the volume of Dorset Blue Vinny declined, and by about 1955 commercial production had probably ceased altogether. Nevertheless a certain mystique had grown up around it and stories abounded of it still being produced on small farms in secluded Dorset valleys known only to the principal restaurateurs serving the delicacy. Articles about these lucky people who were able to find it appeared from time to time in local journals or the gourmet sections of the national Sunday newspapers, and in magazines catering for those who liked exotic, rare or expensive food and drink. At the same time, it appeared that one could in any number of Dorset pubs eat good, filling and creamy blue cheese which the publicans described as Dorset Blue Vinny, Blue Vinny, and Dorset Blue.

These stories were quite misleading and were written to satisfy a demand which some townspeople had for distinctive, natural country fare. They shrouded a brisk trade in second-grade Stiltons which were transported in lorries from Leicestershire down to Dorset in considerable quantities, there to be sold at prices which were often greater than for first-grade Stilton. It was a case of people being willing to pay more for a second-class product than they would have done for a first-class one, if it were presented to them under a different name, in fancy wrapping and with misleading publicity. No doubt it happens all the time.

The lid was blown off this particular racket in a Court case held in Reading at which Dr John G. Davis was a witness. The so-called Dorset Blue Vinny which had been sold for years turned out to be a nice soft tasty cheese having 30 to 32 per cent fat content. It was laid down by the Court that while any blue-veined cheese could be labelled 'Blue Vinny' or 'Dorset Blue', the term 'Dorset Blue Vinny' could only be used for a blue-veined cheese made in Dorset from skimmed milk, and having no more than 15 per cent fat content.

That seemed to be my cue. Why not make genuine Dorset Blue Vinny? If I succeeded in doing so, there should be no risk of competition, and I could make as much as the market would take. Not that I expected to make more than 100 to 200 tons annually, but that was enough to utilise my surplus milk. It might even enable me to buy in some milk to fulfil a demand.

My first step was to get Dr John Davis down to explain to Mike and Dorothy Harp how to make the cheese. The next was to prepare a small cottage near Ashley Dairy for its production and storage, and to get in whatever equipment was necessary. I thought it sensible to keep its manufacture well away from the Cheddar dairy because the mould that we wanted to encourage for the Dorset Blue Vinny would have been ruinous to the Cheddar. The half-mile that in fact separated the cottage where the Blue Vinny was made from the Cheddar dairy was only just sufficient to my over-anxious mind to preserve us from the danger of phage.

So Dorset Blue Vinny began to be made again in a commercial way for the first time in twenty-seven years. We made it in round wheel-shaped cheeses weighing about ten pounds a piece which we stored in a room in the cottage in a damp cool atmosphere, secured by pouring buckets of water on the floor and building up the humidity so as to encourage the development of the blue mould. We showed the cheese to the wife of an old farmer who herself had made the same cheese years ago in the Bride Valley, and asked her opinion of it. After inspecting, prodding and tasting it, she testified that we were following the same method that she had used, and that the cheese we were making tasted just as it used to.

All this was very reassuring until we discovered that not all the cheese we were making managed to retain the blue mould for the seven or eight weeks it was supposed to be stored before being eaten. It tasted all right but simply did not turn blue. We could no doubt sell it as a miniature 'Dorset White', thus inaugurating a wholly new gastronomic experience, but if we did that we could hardly claim that we had resuscitated the famed Dorset Blue Vinny.

There were two reasons for our partial failure. The first was that we were using pasteurised milk, while the old Dorset Blue Vinny-makers used non-pasteurised milk and made their cheese in the most unhygienic conditions. There were stories of it being stored with the saddlery and farming implements in the old days, in conditions which suited the proliferation of all kinds of bacteria, including mould. The result could be such a ripe cheese that its eaters would watch the maggots in it race each other down the dining-room table. We, however, prided ourselves on our cleanliness, and thus provided a pretty hostile environment to bugs and mould.

The other trouble concerned the cottage. As it was not purpose built for a cheese dairy, we were unable to provide a constant cool and humid atmosphere regardless of the weather outside. What was more, we were running a risk, with all the water we were splashing on the walls and floor to maintain the humidity, of causing its collapse.

Cheddar and Blue Vinny

I decided therefore to build a special dairy for the further development of this cheese which was proving so tantalizingly difficult to make. I sited it at Higher Kingston Russell Farm, some two miles away, as the crow flies, from the Cheddar dairy at Parks Farm. An old corn barn was converted to provide a proper cheese diary where the humidity and temperature could be scientifically controlled. It cost me £30,000, and unfortunately did not qualify for a grant under the government's new Business Promotion Scheme because it was not in the right area.

Production began anew and this time, after much trial and error, good Dorset Blue Vinny was consistently produced. An article in the local *Dorset Echo* was picked up by *The Times* and we were overwhelmed with publicity. Two television films were made about this new enterprise, one by South West Television and the other by Channel 4. Both involved a whole afternoon of filming with a camera crew of seven or eight men and an interviewer, and resulted in no more than ten minutes of film. An interview with me, lasting fifteen to twenty minutes, about the development of the estate finished up as two minutes of film which drew particular attention to the low-fat quality of the cheese. The stars of this particular film were Mike and Dorothy Harp who were shown watching the skimmed milk being poured into a vat and then inspecting the cheeses shown ripening in the store.

The result of the publicity was a renewed stirring of interest in the cheese. Orders were received for it from as far as Scotland and quite a lot was sold to wholesalers who distributed it to various London stores and shops specializing in unusual cheeses and other foods. This should have spelt success for the product, but it did not.

Popularity with the specialized food shops should, one might think, make such an enterprise profitable, but we discovered that that was not so. First of all, their profit margins on individual products seemed to be too high. Secondly, their combined buying power did not amount to much. One day I was told that a very well-known Westminster cheese shop was stocking our Dorset Blue Vinny. Feeling somewhat elated at this, I went along to buy some from it. The price was £4.95 a pound. As we had sold it to the wholesaler at £1.80 a pound, I was moved to say to the shop assistant that it seemed very expensive. 'Ah, but it's a rare cheese,' I was told. 'Yes,' I remarked to myself, 'and you are contributing to make it so.'

Another difficulty was its keeping quality. Its shelf-life, if unopened, was about three to four weeks. Once opened, it had to be eaten within a week. While people normally buy Cheddar by the pound or half-pound, their purchases of blue cheese are usually in much smaller quantities, so that demand for a ten pound cheese had to be good to prevent the opened cheese from deteriorating.

We were carried away by the enthusiasm shown for the cheese in the most unlikely places and did not realize, until it was too late, that without supermarket support, the volume of sales to justify commercial production did not exist. The supermarkets we approached said that the public they served was not adventurous in trying new foods and that it was not their function to educate people's palates.

We had over-produced and made more than we could sell. Although butter was made from the cream from the milk, a loss was made during the two years we were producing Dorset Blue Vinny and so, to my regret, we ceased making it in the Summer of 1985. Even now I hope that the cessation will prove temporary and that some supermarket chain will eventually be found willing to take sufficient quantities of the cheese to justify a renewal of production. Our experience showed that enterprise does not always pay off.

Ever since 1928, farm buildings, though not farm houses, have been derated. The reason for this was a desire on the part of government to prevent the farming industry, in deep trouble from subsidized imports, from going under completely. Since about 1960 and particularly since entry into the Common Market, most farmers are considerably better off than they were, and the attitude of the political parties towards derating agricultural buildings has changed.

The Labour Party is frankly in favour of rating farm buildings, and the Alliance parties seem now to take the same view. The Labour Party realizes that most of its potential voters reside in the cities or in suburbia and that they have little to lose by attacking the agricultural interest. The Conservative Party, which still supports derating of farm buildings, also draws most of its support from the cities and suburbia but retains most of the rural districts, albeit with their much sparser population. It is not an issue on which they want to encourage controversy, for it could easily set up strains between the majority of their urban and suburban voters, who might well think that their rates bill would go down if farm buildings were rated, and their rural supporters who benefit by the present situation.

This was the political framework subsisting when in 1980 we, to our surprise, were told by the Valuation Officer for the rating area of West Dorset that he had sought to enter assessments in the valuation list in respect of our cheese dairy, which he proposed to assess at a rateable value of £1,350. To justify his action he called our cheese dairy a factory and evidently thought that the size of our operation justified his initiative. But the Rating Act 1971 is quite clear on the matter. Section 26 states that (i) No agricultural land or agricultural buildings shall be liable to be rated or be included in any valuation list or in any rate. And Section 26 (4) (b) goes on to say that this 'includes a building which is used solely in connection with agricultural operations carried on on agricultural land and which is occupied by the occupiers of all that land.'

There was no doubt that I occupied all the land, that this land was principally devoted to rearing dairy cattle, and that their milk went into the cheese dairy where it was processed into tip-top Cheddar cheese and whey-butter. This would seem to be an obvious agricultural operation carried out on what was clearly agricultural land.

How on earth could the rating valuer deny the evidence of his eyes and call it a factory, thereby meaning an industrial under-taking? When the case came before the Dorset Local Valuation Court, we found out his process of reasoning. He must have had a romantic side to his imagination, and saw farming activities through a misty haze of ancient folklore and story. Of course cheesemaking was an agricultural operation, but only if carried on by a farmer's wife in a picturesque cottage and producing a few pounds of Cheddar daily from the surplus milk. In his view, an operation employing seven people full-time which produced, as we did then, 450 tons of Cheddar a year from 1,000,000 gallons of milk was not an agricultural but an industrial enterprise, and to confuse the issue he adduced the cases of broiler houses set up on a few acres of land, factories for turning corn into breakfast cereals, pigs into sausages, and mills for turning grain into flour. What he was in effect saying was that small-scale peasant farming was, but large-scale modern farming was not, an agricultural rather than an industrial enterprise.

The Valuation Court did not entertain such arguments and gave judgement to me and Streatfeild Hood and Company Limited, who were joined with us in the action. The Valuation Officer appealed to the Lands Tribunal, and two years later we had the satisfaction of learning that his appeal had been thrown out. But until the day of that judgement I had been made to pay the rates which the Lands Tribunal had just decided were illegal. I got them back, though without interest.

The importance of this victory to the farming community as a whole cannot be exaggerated. For a start, about 220 farmhouse cheesemakers up and down the country would have been immediately affected had the Valuation Officer won his case. But no one would have expected the rating authorities to stop there.

They undoubtedly would have proceeded to rate calf-houses, piggeries and probably dairies, on the argument that the scale of the operation no longer conformed to traditional views of farming, and that it was no more than another form of industrial production.

I believe that the firmness with which Streatfeild Hood and we faced this attempt to rerate farm buildings by a back-door approach has saved the farming interest tens of millions of pounds a year.

Another venture started in 1982 also proved more attractive in theory than it ever did in practice. This was a retailing enterprise. We thought it would be a good idea to retail from the farm the products that we produced on it, such as Cheddar cheese, Dorset Blue Vinny, butter and cream. However, to encourage enough people to come to make it worthwhile, it was necessary to put up signs on the main road to indicate where we were, and this the police did not allow for fear of it causing traffic accidents. It was therefore necessary to look for a shop in a village, but that alone would not suffice. It had to have enough forecourt facing the road to enable cars to park.

The ideal place was a petrol station, which would have a large forecourt and also act as a magnet for people to stop at. As a result of these considerations, I became a lessee of the Esso Company at their recently vacated petrol station at Winterbourne Abbas on the A35, five miles west of Dorchester. It was my first real contact with the oil industry and the terms they dictated were onerous. The margin between purchase and sale of petrol was only between 5p and 6p per gallon, which contrasted with about 20 cents in the United States for a smaller gallon. In addition they wanted the lessee to accept credit cards, which would effectively reduce the gross margin to about 3p or 3½p a gallon. Further, and this perhaps was the meanest cut of all, one had to pay by direct debit for the petrol the moment it was pumped into the tanks, while of course one did not wholly recover the price of it for three or four weeks. For anyone to take on a lease on such terms was in effect to volunteer to operate a continuous treadmill, the hard labour once meted out to Chinese convicts. The screw was further tightened by the banks, possibly the ones to have profited most out of post-war governments' addiction to inflation and high interest rates, for they proceeded to make charges of up to £3,000 per annum merely for the privilege of paying money into them.

The petrol company's intention was that its lessee would break even, if he was lucky, in the sale of petrol, and would be able to earn his bread by extraneous activities carried out on the site, such as selling motor accessories and confectionery. Our intention was to do just that, and in addition to convert a line of ruined holiday chalets into a farm shop. This we did, and soon, instead of a long ugly concrete block, there was a mini-food store in yellow and white with Georgian bay-windows fronting the road. We secured the services of another part of the Thacker family to run this complex, their eldest daughter Brenda with her husband Trevor.

Soon this farm shop, which stocked a large variety of food as well as our own cheese and butter, was known over quite a wide area of West Dorset. It was the largest food shop in the fifteen miles between Dorchester and Bridport. With the petrol, turnover was high, though profit was non-existent. After three years it began to turn in a small profit, although I keep it going not for that but because it fulfils a service, and gives a certain amount of employment to the neighbourhood.

CHAPTER *12*

Quotas

By 1980 we had come to realize that if we continued to follow our existing policy of meeting our own needs for dairy cow replacements from our own stock of heifers, the dairy cow population on our existing 2,350 acres could not exceed 1,200. At the time there was no limit to milk production save one's own resources and one's efficiency at coaxing milk from the cows.

I was not altogether satisfied with this, partly because cheese production depended on milk yield, partly because it signified the end of our headlong and almost continuous expansion of the estate. I remained in good health and that for me was synonymous with activity. I had other fields of interest into which to throw myself but the development of Ashley Chase had a curious fascination for me. Perhaps it was that it came to be an extension of my personality. It certainly offered continual problems which had to be surmounted, and a continuation of successes, small enough in themselves, but collectively seen as milestones, in a by no means negligible achievement.

Nevertheless, with the recovery of land prices, I was not particularly keen to incur more debt by buying up land at £2,200 to £2,600 an acre. What I hoped for was that some farmer, getting fed up with having continually to milk his cows in all seasons, would join me in a profit-sharing arrangement which would

Cedric Littman at Watergate House with the Bride flowing through the garden

John and Joan Thacker

Snow on the Chesil

enable us to keep a dairy going on his land without his granting me a tenancy and thus halving its value.

In 1981, another of those perennial financial crises hit the country. The government's reaction to it was to raise interest rates. Base rate rose to 16 per cent which meant that borrowers were having to pay from 18 per cent to 21 per cent per annum interest. It happened that this crisis caught John Eversden at an awkward time. He had made for himself a tidy fortune by trading in almost everything one could need in the agricultural world, and six months previously had brought together a little consortium to buy the 350 acres of Cruxton Manor Farm with the idea, no doubt, of breaking it up and selling it in due course, piecemeal. But the sudden rise in base rate and a murky financial outlook in general had caused a sudden fall in land values, and the members of this consortium were anxious to extricate themselves from their investment. John rang me up to ask if I could be interested. Strangely enough, we had inspected Cruxton Manor Farm about twelve years before when it had consisted of about 550 acres, and was rather larger than now. I had turned it down then because it seemed to me that the dairy was wrongly situated, but also because Higher Kingston Russell, which was much closer and easier to farm, had suddenly come on the market.

Cruxton Manor Farm possessed a somewhat restored Jacobean manor, which I did not want, but it had a complete set of dairy buildings for 200 dairy cattle, with barns that had been filled with silage by Eversden's sons. The advantage of acquiring it lay in the fact that, apart from a new parlour which would have to be installed, I could start milking there straight away. The consortium was in a quandary. It was a dairy farm but they had no dairy cattle to utilise its facilities. They had obviously not counted on farming it, and now land prices had fallen. They wanted £1,600 an acre for the farm with the manor house. Within a few days terms had been agreed. Eversden would keep the manor house for himself for the time being and I would buy the 350-acre farm at £1,250 an acre. Its purchase would land me in further expenditure of £500,000, it was true, but within two years I could see another 220-cow dairy being milked there and producing a further 250,000 gallons of milk annually.

A few days after I had paid the deposit, I was walking on one of the hills along the farm's western boundary when I saw flames leaping across the ground on the opposite hillside, and clouds of smoke rising in the sky. I walked over, wondering if someone had committed an act of careless vandalism which might spread towards the buildings, when I saw John Thacker and Ernest Chaffey emerging from the smoke. They were simply burning the stubble preparatory to new cultivations. They were not letting the grass grow under their feet. John had sought Eversden's permission to introduce our cattle and to start ploughing the moment he heard contracts had been exchanged. We quickly installed a modern processor-controlled eight-a-side herringbone milking parlour and, by November of the same year, had a herd of eighty milkers on it. The dairyman was Bim Wrixon, a Wraxall farmer's son who had married Jane Thacker. He was as good a dairyman as any we had on the estate, and he and Jane were happy to move out of their modern cottage at Litton, where he had been head dairyman, to the old rambling cottage in which they made their home on the lonely hillside overlooking the Frome. The next Winter we had 200 dairy cows there.

This farm purchase was a bargain, allowing for the change in value of money, for it probably cost no more than two-thirds of what it would have fetched twelve years earlier. Without its dairy-buildings and four houses, the cost of the bare land to me was probably less than £900 an acre. There was little building to be done, and we could, and did, walk in to work it immediately.

Until the Spring of 1984, our particular economic goal at Ashley Chase was to build up milk production and to convert as much of that milk as we were allowed into cheese. Like everyone else we had heard of milk-lakes and butter-mountains but they seemed to concern other countries and not Britain, and other farmers rather than us. After all, Britain was not even self-sufficient in milk products, for we still only produced about 80 per cent of all the milk products we consumed, while for our part, we sold every pound of cheese and butter on the market, and not into Intervention. Something had to be done about these surpluses, it was true, but should it be done to those who were not even self-sufficient, rather than to those like France who produced twice as much milk products as they consumed? Neither government nor our own National Farmers Union gave us an inkling of what was in store for us when, on 31 March 1984, a system of milk quotas was announced.

The terms were distinctly unfavourable to Britain and absolutely punishing for British dairy farmers. Britain had to reduce its milk output by 6 per cent, while France had its milk production reduced by only 2 per cent. Holland, which produced over 122 per cent of its home consumption, had its production cut by a relatively small amount, while Eire, which produced over 164 per cent of its consumption, was actually allowed to increase production by 5 per cent.

If the reductions within the different Common Market countries seemed unfairly distributed, the method of implementing the new scheme was positively villainous. I do not think that one can fairly question a system of quotas during a period of over-production. The alternative is a deliberate price squeeze which

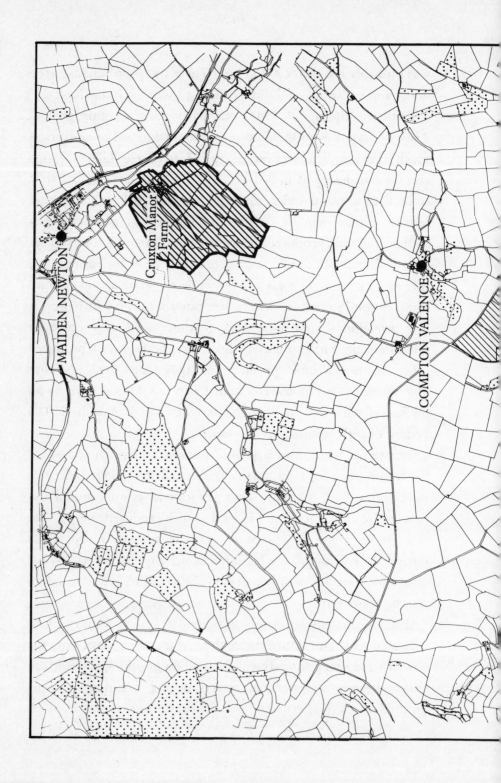

MAIDEN NEWTON

Cruxton Manor Farm

COMPTON VALENCE

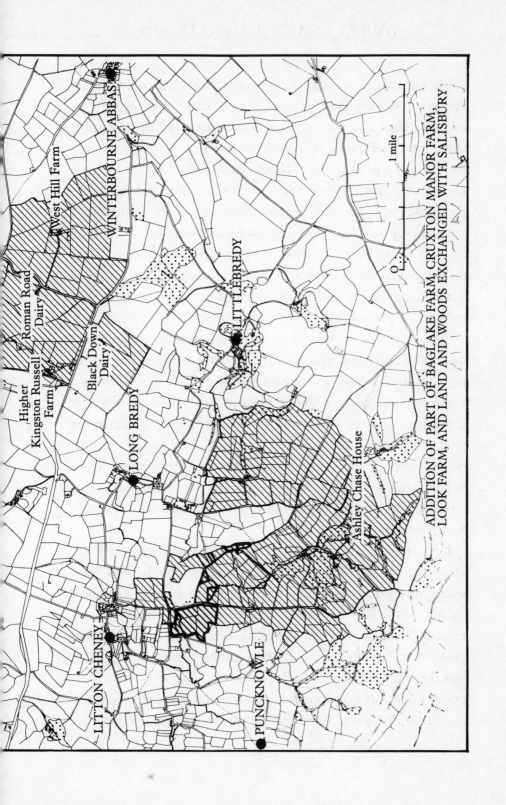

ADDITION OF PART OF BAGLAKE FARM, CRUXTON MANOR FARM, LOOK FARM, AND LAND AND WOODS EXCHANGED WITH SALISBURY.

West Hill Farm

WINTERBOURNE ABBAS

Higher Kingston Russell Farm

Roman Road Dairy

Black Down Dairy

LONG BREDY

LITTLEBREDY

Ashley Chase House

LITTON CHENEY

PUNCKNOWLE

0   1 mile

might not only prove ruinous to many farmers but could quickly convert a surplus into a shortage that might then prove permanent. What a farmer requires, however, is sufficient warning that a system of quotas is about to be imposed. Dairying requires fairly long-term planning. Suitable land, proper buildings and a good stable milking herd take years to assemble and to form a profitable milking unit. Changes sufficiently drastic to produce a reduction by 6 per cent of milk yield normally require a year or so to plan. Cows have a nine-month gestation followed by two to three months' rest. Dairies therefore run on an annual cycle with silage being grown and stored, concentrate being bought, and milk yields planned over a period of a year.

For a Minister of Agriculture therefore suddenly to impose a quota system on the national herd which was to operate within eighteen days showed a disregard for the dairy farmer which was virtually unprecedented since the war. It was worse than that for those dairy farmers who went beyond mere milk production and who either bottled and delivered their milk direct to the consumer or converted it into cheese and butter on their farms. These unfortunates were not to know of the amount of reduced output to be inflicted upon them until nine months into the year for which quotas were applicable.

It is not surprising that panic hit the whole dairy industry. Dairy cows that were averaging £570 a cow in March 1984 were averaging £490 a cow in July of that year. The national dairy herd shrank. Some farmers simply sold their herds for slaughter, the carcases going to swell the stores of meat in Intervention. Some plunged into bankruptcy and many suffered great losses. In the end the stampede out of milk production was so great that the country did not even produce enough milk to reach its quota, reduced as that was to 6 per cent of the previous year's production.

In the end therefore no penalties were levied, but much hardship was caused.

No one in the dairy industry could really understand how a British Minister of Agriculture could bring himself to treat the industry in this manner. The old confrontation between the welfare of an alleged agricultural work-force of only 3 per cent and the mythical 'consumer', which of course includes everyone, was trotted out by the Minister and the government. This argument could of course be used to destroy every industry in the Kingdom, ultimately leaving the consumer to live upon imported goods paid for out of money received from welfare payments. Possibly, the trade-off was even more cynical: a quick sell-out of the dairy farmer for a lump-sum rebate promised to the British Government out of Common Market funds which may have amounted to £450,000,000, which could then be trumpeted as a victory for British toughness towards its Common Market partners.

The year 1983–4, bedevilled by quotas and threats by the Milk Marketing Board of penalties for over-production, helped to cut our profit before interest to half the record profit achieved in 1982–3. In common with many others, we met the problem by cutting down the ration of concentrate instead of reducing the numbers of our cattle, with the result that not only did yields drop, but gross margins fell. Before the year was out, however, we hit on a way to deal with this particular problem. We converted one of our eight dairies to raising beef, and fed the rest of the herd in the proper way. The result was that within two years of the commencement of quotas we were getting just as much milk from our 1,200 cows in seven dairies as we had been getting previously from eight.

We then hit upon another expedient for improving production, buying quota. We purchased for just under 12p a litre some 500,000 litres (110,000 gallons) from another farmer in Sussex who was reducing his milking herd. So I paid £59,000 for the privilege of producing a quantity of milk which, two years before, I had possessed as a right. It might seem daft to the layman but it was a recognized way of counterbalancing the effect of quotas. Thus, after having our permitted milk production cut from 1,468,000 gallons to 1,368,000 gallons, we were able to get back more or less to the old figure plus a little more. It was a method of paddling hard to stay in the same place.

A good example of a way the Ministry of Agriculture made people run around at considerable cost and to no advantage, simply as a result of their haste in imposing quotas and a lack of foresight, is well illustrated by the story I shall now unfold.

In the year 1982 we overshot our datum by 120,000 lb of cheese. We offered to pay a penalty but the Milk Marketing Board refused this and actually reduced our datum for the following year! The milk we were prevented from converting into cheese was then sold to the Milk Marketing Board.

I could have been philosophical about that, but not about what then followed. Our arms were, metaphorically speaking, twisted. We were incessantly warned by the Milk Marketing Board that if we did not voluntarily reduce our cheese production further, the whole production of the Farmhouse Cheesemakers Association might be cut. By alternate threats and cajolery, they succeeded in reducing our cheese production for 1983 to 508 tons in comparison with 659 tons in 1982.

Then, when quotas were imposed, they came under two distinct headings, Primary Direct Sales Quota, which referred to the milk which we processed into cheese, and Primary Wholesale Quota, which referred to milk sold to the Milk Marketing Board.

This division was based on what one had done in the calendar year 1983, which happened to be the year when we had been forced to sell on the liquid market, and had converted only 1,117,371 gallons into cheese, and sold 312,508 gallons to the Board. The two sets of quotas were not considered interchangeable, and the pattern was set.

The effect on our cheese production was devastating. Our production of milk was about 250,000 gallons above our datum for Cheddar sold on the home market, so that the imposition of a 6 per cent reduction on milk production would not, in the normal way, have affected our cheese production. But by imposing a 6 per cent cut on each type of sale and treating the two types of milk disposal which we were forced into in the quota year 1984 as permanent, we suffered a 13 per cent cut in our cheese production, and were more or less back where we had been in 1980 before we had been given our 13 per cent increase in datum. This made nonsense of our purchase of Cruxton Manor Farm, which had been bought not merely for the purpose of raising milk production but of raising cheese production. Such a result had not been the intention of the quota system, and we had certainly not expected it to work that way.

A system of tribunals had been set up by the Minister to hear hardship cases, and as I thought we qualified as such if anyone did, I lost little time in putting in my appeal. Months later, my case was heard by the Somerset Tribunal sitting in Taunton. Despite my being ill at the time, I attended and put my own case. Each tribunal was composed of three members, and each one of those members agreed that I had a good case, and that they would recommend the Minister to allow me to treat my 1984 milk sales as Primary Direct Sales; in other words to treat the two types of quota as interchangeable.

Many weeks later I received a tribunal decision from the Chairman of the Dairy Produce Quota Tribunal for England and Wales. He had not heard the evidence, but had merely received the papers and advice from the Somerset Tribunal. He simply threw out my case, but recommended me to investigate with the Milk Marketing Board the possibilities for exchanging any unused Wholesale Quota for Direct Sales Quota under the MMB 'Swop-Shop' arrangement. This arrangement did not effectively exist owing to the fact that a lot more people wanted Direct Sales Quota than wanted Wholesale Quota.

Nevertheless, some time later a rescript went out from the Milk Marketing Board stating that there would be flexibility of quota for at least two years. For that period, then, I would not be penalized in the way I had feared. Many months after that we found that if the requisite forms were filled in, this temporary flexibility could be converted to a permanent flexibility, and we would be back to the position we had been in some two years before.

The amount of time and money spent on this rigmarole, to cover up the EEC's carelessness and craven subservience to political direction, was enormous. The whole story affords a good illustration of the inanities of politicians and the political system under which they function, which gives priority to the wishes of an uninformed and ignorant electorate, capable of being swayed overnight by blatantly misleading propaganda, over the proper interests of various industries and classes of people, and the good of the country as a whole.

The final chapter in this saga of government ineptitude has not yet been mentioned. Two years later the Milk Marketing Board, which had had its arm twisted by the Ministry of Agriculture, admitted that its whole system of control of cheese production, by fixing limits on how much cheese a farmhouse cheesemaker could make, was contrary to the Treaty of Rome and therefore illegal. From April 1 1986, regulatory datums on cheese-making would cease. That year we increased production by nearly 20 per cent and sold the entire increase on the home market.

CHAPTER *13*

Friends and Neighbours

The population of the Bride Valley and its immediate surroundings, for the most part, is comprised of three groups: the landowners and farmers who own or farm the land; those who work for them on the land; and people who live in the villages but work in town, coupled with those who have retired to the country after a career spent in industry and commerce.

The last category come increasingly to occupy the old cottages in the villages and the new houses that have been built in them over the last ten years, and their presence has resulted in doubling the population of villages such as Litton Cheney and Puncknowle. It is partly due to their coming that village cottages, which twenty years ago fetched about £5,000, now sell for £40,000 to £60,000, and make it virtually impossible for farmworkers and artisans attached to the ancillary trades to buy them.

These newcomers lead a pleasant social life among themselves, centred around the parish church and each other's houses, but are often strangely oblivious of the life of the farms and fields which tightly hem them in and form their horizon on every side. They are often even unaware of the crops that are grown or what is done with milk drawn from the cattle seen from their windows on the adjacent pastures. Some of them do not even know of the existence of the cheese dairy which operates only half a mile from them, and whose lights they can see, if they are awake, from four in the morning. So the villages, despite their inflated population and their new buildings, give a false impression of rural prosperity. They are no longer filled with an active population working on the land and in the trades required to buttress farming production, but have become in part dormitory villages for those working elsewhere, or places of repose for prosperous retired townsmen. One of the results of this trend is that farmers have to recruit part of their workforce from towns like Bridport, or build houses for them on their own land, cottages which are then 'tied' to the job and vacated on leaving it.

Farmworkers tend to keep to themselves, particularly those who live in farm cottages. Their main meeting-place is the local pub, particularly when the latter has the additional amenity of a skittles alley. In order to promote social life and foster a sense of community, David and Ian Thacker organized a skittles team called the Ashley Chasers which exhibited its prowess in that sport in the Bride Valley Skittles League. In Summer a cricket team was formed for the same purpose. But Ashley Chase is a large, somewhat scattered estate which takes half an hour to traverse from north to south by car, and many who lived and worked at one end did not even know some of those who lived and worked at the other.

To attempt to remedy this we revived the old village institution of the harvest festival. It had almost fallen into desuetude when we came to Ashley Chase. Some time in late August or September, Joan Thacker would lead a team of volunteers, mostly comprising her own family, and a big barn or the tractor-shed would be emptied and cleaned. Straw bales would be arranged around three sides and a long trestle-table laden with chicken, tongue, ham, sausage rolls, salads, trifles and cakes on the fourth side. Entertainment would be provided, which varied from year to year. Sometimes there would be a film show for the children and a skittles alley for the adults; sometimes a troupe of Morris dancers or Clog and Barn dancers would keep everyone entertained until midnight.

Up to one hundred and thirty people attended these harvest festivals. Everyone who worked on the estate was invited with their families and the occasion did something to get people to know one another and to promote a feeling of friendship among those who lived and worked at Ashley Chase.

Once or twice a year we held great parties at Ashley Chase. About seventy people from the valley and from town would come to the floodlit house, which looked from afar like some Scottish border mansion out of a Walter Scott novel. A four-piece string quartet under the leadership of our District Nurse Channon, a part-time member of the Bournemouth Orchestra, would appear in the gallery and soon the strains of Mozart, Haydn, Bach and Vivaldi would resound from the oak-panelling of the hall, which seemed acoustically perfect. Once we had a troupe who sang and played Restoration songs and music, and came dressed as courtiers of the reign of Charles II. They performed on the stone courtyard outside the illuminated house, and we sat in a circle around them. It was a scene from the past which must have stayed long in the memory of all those who participated in it.

The adjoining landowners and farmers were people with a variety of talent. There was Lionel King who had been Lord of the Manor of Puncknowle, and arriving there in 1948, had proceeded to create a prosperous dairy farm of 750 acres out of once derelict farmland. He had read for the Bar and had been a high-ranking official of the Anglo-Persian Oil Company; he had subsequently farmed in Suffolk and, among other industrial products, had been the manufacturer of the 'Glo-Worm' boiler, that mainstay of Army catering.

He had achieved fame – or should one say notoriety? – on a national scale by taking his rights and duties as Lord of the Manor and squire of his village seriously. There was a spring on his land which, though unpiped, provided the only source of water for the villagers of Puncknowle. Some of the inhabitants of West Bexington, a small village resort on the coast whose water supply was inadequate, campaigned for a better supply to be piped in by the local authority. Bridport was the obvious source of such a supply but that involved several miles of piping and pumping. The local Health Officer, discovering the spring in Puncknowle, thought it would be far more economical to draw water for West Bexington from there. When Lionel King heard this, he bearded the man and asked him what would then happen to the villagers of Puncknowle. He was told that they were an elderly lot who could move out and be rehoused elsewhere. Realizing that if that happened, Puncknowle would disappear as other villages in the Bride Valley had disappeared before, Lionel King fought the proposal in the Courts and the upshot was that Puncknowle not only kept its water but had it piped to each house.

While they were doing that, the Local Authority built the first drainage system the village had ever had, and brought in electricity. It might seem strange that an English village should have to wait till the 1940s for such amenities, which we now take for granted, but it illustrates the recent and rapid impetus of change that has overtaken the more remote villages of England.

Having won his fight for the village, Lionel King proceeded to improve the estate cottages and eliminate most of the public footpaths which criss-crossed his farm and made efficient farming difficult. He exhibited a similar independent and, one might say, truculent spirit when, walking his farm one morning, he was amazed to see the barns, the dairy and his tractors unoccupied. He asked his foreman where everyone was, and was told that 'the mackerel were in'. He discovered that it was the time-honoured custom in the two fishing villages of Abbotsbury and Puncknowle for the men to drop whatever they were doing, and race down to the sea to get their boats and seine nets out, whenever the lookout man posted on Puncknowle Knoll sighted a shoal of mackerel coming in to shore. When his men returned from the Chesil Beach, he coolly informed them that if that happened again, they could look elsewhere for a job. As he was the biggest employer in the village, and the forerunner of the DHSS did not then distribute the kind of largesse for the flimsiest reasons which it does today, it never did happen again. Curiously enough, the shoals of mackerel that used to head for Abbotsbury beach have largely disappeared since then, although more recently it seems that they have been returning to those waters.

Another thing Lionel King noticed when he came to Puncknowle was that virtually everyone in the village seemed to be related to one another, and he did his best to import people from elsewhere to bring variety into the local bloodstream. When his only son died at eighteen, he sold the estate and came to live in the enlarged rectory in Long Bredy, from which vantage point he dispensed advice, to whomever would take it, on modern farming methods. He had a splendid library of historical and biographical works, and the largest library on farming in private hands, with books dating from the time of the first Elizabeth.

He was astonished to find that we were doing all the right

things in farming before taking his advice. He was a somewhat combative man and, paradoxically, he was a violent Socialist and thought that Attlee's government was the best we had had since that of Lloyd George. My political views were diametrically opposed to his, but I shared his keen interest in history and farming, so we spent many an evening in my study at Ashley or in his book-lined library over tea and the excellent cakes which his wife Mary would prepare, and which in those days nothing prevented me from eating.

One Winter's day, he rang me up to say that he was coming over for a chat. In he came and for three hours we conversed and smoked before the fire in my study. Then, at about 8 pm, he jumped into his new car and drove home to dinner. Over an hour later Mary rang me to say that he had just arrived, which was astonishing seeing that he lived but five minutes away by car. I then heard a horrifying tale. He had driven down my country roads up to Tenants Hill and along its crest on a private hardcore road I had built to link up with Abbotsbury Lane, which led into Long Bredy. But he had missed the turning by about ten yards and plunged into a mass of wet mud over a foot deep, in which his car became completely stuck. Suddenly he had been faced with a life-and-death struggle less than a mile from his home and no more than that from the warm and comfortable fireside he had been sitting in front of only five minutes before. He was 600 feet up a hill in the depth of Winter. It was quite cold and completely black. If he kept his engine on, he would have suffocated, unless he opened the window, in which case he might have frozen. Once he turned the car lights off, the blackness was so dense that he could not even see his feet. He was seventy-two and heavily built. Eventually he could make out some lights twinkling in the distance. He reckoned they were those of Lyme Regis, sixteen miles away, and it gave him an indication which way he should go. Struggling with difficulty out of the car, rather than risk spending a frozen night upon the hill, he chose to make for the direction of the lights, which might then lead him to the cottages near our Litton Dairy about half a mile away. But the ground, which he could not see, was uneven. Partly it was rutted and pitted hardcore road, and partly it was uneven grassland fenced here and there by barbed wire or hedges. First he lost his pipe, then his shoes. Then he broke his glasses. He partly walked and partly crawled his way along the crest of the hill and by the time he banged on the window of one of our Litton Dairy cottages, he was in a poor state. Mary told me that after a warm bath, a good whisky and dinner, he was feeling less sorry for himself, but was missing his favourite pipe. So the next morning up I went to trace the route he must have taken, and I brought his pipe back to him in triumph.

I tell this story to illustrate how easy it is for a rural area of hills and valleys, breathtaking in its beauty when conditions are favourable, to turn suddenly menacing once the supports of our modern way of life fail us. A cautious and respectful attitude to the terrain and to the weather means that all goes pleasantly and well, but misjudgement, momentary carelessness and disregard for the land and the elements which surround us can turn a peaceful and well-loved scene into something hostile and even dangerous.

Another man to be remembered is the Reverend Glyn Lewis, the rector of Litton Cheney as well as of the depleted congregations at Puncknowle and Long Bredy. He was the man who had led a national movement of opinion aimed at flattening the slag-heaps after the disaster in his parish at Aberfan, but it was typical of him that I did not learn this fact from him. After some heart trouble he came to the Bride Valley in semi-retirement, although one would not have thought so from the work he did. A gentle, rubicund Welshman, he admitted that he did not subscribe to more than eight or nine of the Thirty-Nine Articles of the Anglican creed, but that did not prevent him from giving himself with devotion to the care of those within his parish, and he was loved throughout the valley. He had an engaging tendency towards absent-mindedness, which would extend to giving the wrong number of the Psalm which the choir was about to sing, or indeed of omitting it altogether, and it was touching to see one or other of his sons, both lawyers, gently correcting him from the front pews. He used to come to our harvest festivals and give the non-denominational grace which preceded the feast. He and his wife Nancy gave a mellow and benign presence to the valley.

I have already mentioned Colonel Christopher (Robin) Wordsworth. He had been a District Commissioner in Sudan and returned to farm in England. At one time he had been the most go-ahead farmer in the Bride Valley with his 100-cow dairy at Baglake, but he devoted himself to other things including the magistracy, and he was Chairman of the Dorchester Bench as well as a prison visitor. He was a son of a Bishop of Salisbury, and a great-grandson of the Bishop of Lincoln who lies buried in that great cathedral in a tomb worthy of a king. The most remarkable thing about him, however, was his face, which was the spitting image of the poet William Wordsworth, from whose brother he was descended.

Another neighbour to whom I have previously referred was Lady Williams, the widow of Sir David Williams, who administered the Bridehead Estate for many years until her son, Sir Philip, took over the reins. She successfully managed the estate through difficult times. Formed in 1809 at Littlebredy, it was the oldest continuous holding of size in the valley. She devoted herself to a variety of public work and became the first woman Sheriff of a County, serving as Sheriff of Dorset.

Good friends were Michael and Elizabeth Pengelly who farmed Gorwell and Wears Farms at the eastern end of the Bride Valley. Michael had been a lecturer at the nearby Agricultural College at Kingston Maurwood and was a prominent councillor on the Dorset County Council, representing the Fleet and its villages. Once at dinner Elizabeth's father, Aubrey Waterman, told me that back in 1953 he had contemplated buying Ashley Chase, but it had looked so remote and abandoned, and had posed such a potential cost to make it habitable, that he had shrunk from it. How glad I was for that.

Other friends and neighbours were Admiral Sir John and Lady Hamilton, who lived over the hill at Abbotsbury. He had been brought up in the Bridport area, and among the fondest memories of his youth were the long walks he had taken over the hills and valleys that now comprise the Ashley Chase estate and its environs. A long Naval career, including service on the China station and the Malta run, and culminating in being NATO Commander-in-Chief for the Mediterranean, had not made him forget his determination to return to live in this unspoilt area of Dorset. On retirement he had bought a house in Abbotsbury, within sight and sound of the sea, and under the lee of St Catherine's Hill with its fourteenth-century chapel on its crest. Under a full moon nothing could be more evocative of the past than to see its silvery light illumine the mediaeval chapel and trace the glistening path it made along the sea. It was a fit and proper place for a sailor to come home to rest. He loved walking and even in his seventies would walk up to ten miles a day on the hills and combes of the Bride Valley, which, he said, had not changed visibly since he was a boy.

Another family with whom we were friendly were the Warrens, Joe and Rosemary, who lived in Litton Cheney. Commander Warren was Curator of the Fleet Air Arm Museum at Yeovilton. We were introduced by Roby who was very friendly with their youngest son, Tim. Then there were Charles and Sally Worthington at Kingston Russell House. He was Chairman of the Ballet Rambert. Many were the combats fought on his or our tennis courts.

We also became friendly with Francis and Sarah Woodhouse who bought the Puncknowle estate from Lionel King, and for a time enlarged it with Berwick Farm whence originated the Russell family which later achieved the Dukedom of Bedford. For a time they rivalled us in acreage and head of dairy cattle, until they retracted while we expanded in the 1970s.

Giles Best, a Crown Court Judge who lived at Whitcombe Farm between Long Bredy and Littlebredy, supervised the Bridehead lake in his spare time and came to inspect our own reservoir when we introduced rainbow trout to it. He instructed Cedric in the mysteries of fly-fishing. Justin and Judy Mallinson farmed lower down the Bride Valley at Bredy Farm, and varied the agricultural life with the formation of a country museum, exhibiting the farming implements of days gone by.

One of our strangest, if most distinguished, neighbours was Reynolds Stone. He was an engraver and painter of national repute and among his designs were the delicate white £5 banknote, and the old stamps. He lived with his wife in the Old Rectory in Litton Cheney where he had a five-acre garden which he made a point of allowing to grow completely wild. A very sensitive and private man, he once walked two miles up the valley which separated his house from mine, and walking into my garden, introduced himself and complained about the disappearance of two pet eels to which he had given shelter in his garden. He attributed their loss to effluent being introduced into the River Bride by my new dairy at Litton. After I had mollified him somewhat on that score, he looked about the garden in which I had recently built my pavilion, pool and fish-pond, and asked me how it felt to be living in paradise. If I remember correctly, I replied that, having no certainty about the next world, I did my best to enjoy this one. Though he was no great mixer in village life, many people well-known in the artistic and literary life of the country beat a path to his rural retreat, including Iris Murdoch, Lord Clark and Lord David Cecil.

Then there were John and Susan Bailey. She belonged to the Foot family who had farmed in the valley for several centuries. He was the headmaster of the primary school at Litton Cheney, which he had brought to a pitch of excellence before he retired. He often told me that the school would have been closed had it not been for the children living on our estate. He was a keen archaeologist and had uncovered the site of a Romano-Celtic temple in the field called Walls a quarter of a mile east of Puncknowle Knoll. He was also a local historian and in his retirement produced an excellent little history of the Bride Valley from Neolithic times to about twenty years ago. It was a great success; the first edition of 1000 copies sold out pretty smartly, and a second edition was printed. There was a fine photograph of Ashley Chase house in it, but nothing else about an estate which comprised about a quarter of the region and which, admittedly very latterly, had been the scene of an agricultural revolution possibly as significant as anything that had taken place in the Bride Valley since men came to settle there.

It was this omission which prompted me to think that an account of this modern revolution in farming over the last twenty years might perhaps be as interesting as an antiquarian's account of the past, and would certainly give a modern slant to the history of this secluded and beautiful yet virtually unknown part of Dorset. John Bailey's historical account may have been one of the reasons which led me to write this book.

Some of our own men deserve mention. There is Charley Miller, a tractor driver, who came to us not long after we began farming and has stayed with us ever since. Built like a bull and made to follow the plough with a team of horses, it must be somewhat frustrating for him to sit in the cab of a tractor all day, but he does it. When we used to build haystacks in the fields, or fill a barn with hay or straw, it was a sight to see him throw a bale from one end of the barn to the other as if it were a pillow.

Then there is Graham Seymour, the husband of our housekeeper Judy. He does everything that comes his way, from tractor-driving and delivering goats' milk to Crewkerne, to painting houses and repairing fences. I was particularly in his debt when one night a fire broke out in a barn and cattle-yard near his cottage. Despite the danger from the toxic fumes, he crawled under the smoke to open the gates and thus save seventy-two young cattle from asphyxiation.

And how can one ever forget Bim Wrixon who married Jane Thacker and became chief dairyman at Cruxton Manor? Bursting with youth and strength, he nevertheless suffered a brain tumour. A successful operation was followed by radiological treatment. Within a day or two of each radiation dose, he would be back on his feet, milking his cows. To witness such courage is one of those more memorable things that association with Ashley Chase has brought us.

CHAPTER *14*

Land and Landownership

Jonathan Swift once wrote that 'whoever could make two ears of corn or two blades of grass to grow upon a spot of ground where only one grew before would deserve better of mankind and do more essential service to his country than the whole race of politicians put together.' On the basis of those sentiments, we have done pretty well, since I believe that the weight of produce emanating from the different farms that now form the Ashley Chase estate amounts to perhaps twelve or fourteen times that which they produced when they were individual farms under different ownership.

Before I came to the Bride Valley, the farms which I subsequently bought were either semi-derelict, as was the case with Ashley Chase itself, Lower Kingston Russell, West Hill and Cruxton Manor; or as with Parks, Baglake and Higher Kingston Russell, were farmed well below their capacity. The total number of people employed on them was twelve, against forty-two full-time and ten part-time people employed today. The total number of dairy cows carried on them was about 200 while it is now 1,200. The annual weight of milk produced on it, now about

176

6,600 tons, is, I believe, at least seven times that produced before, while about 700 tons of Cheddar cheese and whey-butter is produced, against none at all before.

There can be little doubt that had I not concentrated my endeavours in this valley and its neighbourhood, production would have remained much the same as it was before. In fact, it would have been almost certain that by 1984, when the Common Market countries were collectively over-producing milk, this valley would have been particularly hard hit, and some of the farms which now constitute the estate would be producing even less than they did when I bought them. It is also very likely that some of them would still be without water and without roads, as they were when I took them over. In short, the upper part of the Bride Valley and its neighbouring farms would have been producing very little and been in a semi-derelict condition.

Instead of an economy which was almost on a subsistence level, we have increased its fertility and productive capacity enormously. This has been done partly by better drainage and, where necessary, the building of roads and the laying on of water supplies; partly by intensive grazing and the application of vast quantities of natural as well as chemical fertilizer; and partly by the building of large dairies. As a result virtually all its produce is exported out of the valley to towns up and down the country, while 10 per cent of it is even exported overseas. The whole area of four and a half square miles is now a hive of productive capacity where people can work and live comfortably in surroundings of great beauty. It would not be an exaggeration to say that, in agricultural terms, the Ashley Chase estate has brought an agricultural revolution to the farms composing it, greater than any that has ever taken place on them.

Of course there are some people, and they can be pretty vocal, who would deplore all this. For them it would be preferable for such an area to have returned to its natural state, grazing a few hundred sheep and a few score cattle, while the land drains collapsed, wild flowers, thistles and weeds proliferated, and the land was given over once more to roe deer and rabbits, moths, snakes and butterflies. It would have looked 'unspoiled', picturesque and derelict, the delight of nature-lovers and hikers. If such people, and they are mostly townsmen, who think like this eventually have their way with England, then much of the countryside will degenerate to the state it was in during the Middle Ages. Rural poverty and depopulation will proceed apace, and Britain, with its 56,000,000 inhabitants, will have to rely far more heavily than it now does on imported food, always provided that it has the foreign currency to pay for it.

Another school of thought might argue that it is not so beneficial to a country for large farming estates like Ashley Chase to be built up, because it constitutes better social policy to encourage a pattern of smallholders and tenant farmers. That way, it is thought, more people can acquire an interest in farming the land and the rural population will increase.

The desirability of this or that form of landownership, and the political system based on it, have been the stuff of politics and the cause of civil strife from the days of the small Greek States in the classical period to modern times. When the overwhelming majority of a State's population lived in rural communities, and agricultural produce formed by far the major part of that State's wealth, it was understandable that it should do so.

It might be well, at this stage, to provide a short historical account of farming in England for the benefit of the uninformed critic of the current pattern of land ownership. Land in England in the Middle Ages was the source of military power. The feudal system, which was superimposed on the manorial farms, was a method of making each Lord of a Manor responsible for providing a varying number of armed men for military service to his feudal superiors for a fixed period every year.

The manorial farm, subject to the Lord's rights, was a village partnership through which the land was farmed in common. Farming within the manor was on a subsistence level and almost all the produce of the land was consumed in the village. There was little improvement in farming methods from the thirteenth to the seventeenth century, and many such manors, through soil exhaustion, actually produced less in the later period than they did in the earlier.

With land cultivated in separate and scattered unenclosed strips, and subject to rights of common grazing from August to February, no Winter crops could be grown, drainage was impossible, stock-rearing was a hazardous occupation and improvements of any kind, being dependent on unanimous agreement and the willingness of all to play their part, were practically impossible. In its favour, it should be said that the system enabled a great part of a relatively small national population to be fed, except in times of famine, and housed, however primitively. It also gave them a sense of community in a society, even though this was restricted to the limits of their village and its lands.

Farming for revenue was virtually a matter only for the great estates owned by the large monastic foundations. They farmed on a large scale. Their overseers were familiar with the agricultural treatises of Classical times and with contemporary farming practices in other countries. They had the capital to invest in sizeable schemes of land reclamation, enclose land and drain it, improve the quality of herds and flocks, and erect large barns for winter storage. It was they who, in the main, provided the wool which was the staple of English exports for centuries.

ASHLEY CHASE: *A Dorset Domain*

The feudal system began to break down slowly from the fourteenth century as money circulated more freely, and its decline was precipitated by the several visitations of the plague we know as the Black Death, which reduced the size of the population by about one-third, thus increasing the bargaining power of a depleted labour force. Concomitantly, Lords of Manors began to commute service in kind for money rents, and separate ownerships began to be carved out of manorial land. By the time of the dissolution of the monasteries in 1538, rents had largely replaced services on most farms, and farming slowly began to take on a capitalistic aspect. The bigger landowners farmed for profit in the form of rents, and the farmers relied on selling at least some of their crops, either to pay rent or to buy improvements in their standard of living. But these large farmers existed side by side with the open-field system which ensured that much of England was farmed ineptly, and a good part of it remained in a state of utter neglect, covered with swamps, poor woodlands and heaths.

It was only in the eighteenth century, by which time the landed gentry had become the dominant class, controlling the House of Commons, the government and the magistrature, when land titles were secured and political rulers safe, that great improvements in agriculture could be effected. This was achieved by enclosing land, that is to say by bringing into individual ownership and contiguous blocks land that was formerly subject to rights of common pasturage and cut into strips for individual tillage. This was followed by heavy investment in improvements.

This investment was at first the work of great landowners like Viscount Townshend in Norfolk, Lord Halifax in Surrey, and the fourth and fifth Dukes of Bedford in their work of reclaiming the Fen country, and Coke of Norfolk. They invested great sums in large-scale drainage works, brought in new crops like roots and improved grasses from Flanders and Holland, who were two centuries in advance of us in agricultural methods, and reclaimed enormous areas of waste land. This they did through drainage, manuring, drilling new crops, building better farm buildings and cottages, and introducing better methods of stock-breeding and improved agricultural implements. They carried out the new experimental theories of cattle breeders like Robert Bakewell, chemists like Humphrey Davy, agricultural writers such as Arthur Young, and inventors like Jethro Tull.

The bigger farmers soon followed their example and the result was a tremendous revolution in British farming, which in the period from 1760–1874 was able not merely to feed a population which had virtually quadrupled, but to attain an excellence and, apart from periodic slumps, a prosperity that was the envy of other lands. Its farming methods and cattle breeds were exported to America and the Antipodes and it was the centre of ever-renewed scientific advances in crops, stock-breeding, land drainage and methods of reviving soil fertility.

In the process the English peasantry, which had been associated with the mediaeval system of farming in common, virtually died out, and was replaced with farmers owning an increasingly large individual acreage, farming for cash profits, and utilizing the latest advances in agricultural science, while investing more and more capital in improving their land and increasing their revenue.

Contrary to what uninformed Utopians might think, this agricultural revolution – which resulted in the transformation of a mediaeval British agriculture, farming on a subsistence level and requiring the effort of over three-quarters of the population to feed 750,000 million people, to a highly mechanized and vastly more efficient agriculture able to provide four-fifths of the temperate-grown food needed to feed 56,000,000 people – has owed next to nothing to the smallholder and to the part occupier of common land, but has been the work of capitalist farmers, following the example of the great landowners.

The attitude of the smallholder and the part occupier of common land to this revolution was epitomized by the attempts of the Fenland dwellers in the seventeenth and eighteenth centuries to destroy the canals and drainage system which the fourth and fifth Dukes of Bedford had initiated at great cost with the help of Dutch engineers, and the insular repugnance displayed by small farmers in the seventeenth and eighteenth centuries to foreign crops and foreign methods, shown in the saying, 'They won't grow here with us, for our forefathers never used them.'

Those who think that an ideal countryside would be one dotted with small farms in individual ownership are therefore dreaming about an economy which never existed in England in modern times, and one which could in modern conditions never supply the food we need, nor provide an adequate living to those who might practise it. It is tantamount to believing in a revival of compulsory archery practice on the village greens of England to provide the basis of a body of infantry to defend the realm.

This is not to say that there is no room for the small farmer who wishes to find a niche for himself in agriculture and is willing to offer unremitting labour and suffer a lower standard of living than he might obtain in other ways, in return for a life of independence lived on his own land. It is quite possible at certain times and in certain districts for a skilled smallholder to earn a living in, say, fruit-farming, market-gardening, or calf-rearing, and it is not at all impossible that we might develop here, as in Germany, a breed of part-time farmers who have, as an adjunct to their main non-farming activity, a smallholding on which they and their families can earn a very useful additional income.

The landlord and tenant system is the best way of providing a channel of investment in agricultural land while simultaneously allowing vigorous and enterprising young men, without much capital, to start on the farming ladder. If this system could be disembarrassed of some of the clogs that an ill-advised legislature has seen fit to hobble it with, it could resume its place as the principal means of owning and farming the land. If land owner-ship subject to agricultural tenancies were to be considered as much a farming business as farming with land in hand, as far as taxation on income and succession duties are concerned, and if tenants were given adequate compensation for improvements effected by them but denied a tenancy for their life and that of their families when they take up a term of years, this system of farming land would surely regain its old popularity.

The great Utopian schemes of our century have been largely Marxist in character and have favoured the expropriation of all private ownership in farmland, whether big or small, and their replacement by State ownership. The ostensible reason given for such an enormous act of expropriation has been a thirst for equality, the desire to raise the living standards of the agricultural labouring class, and a desire to improve the productivity of the land. The results have been quite different, and not surprisingly so, since all tyrants from time immemorial have always cloaked their aims with professions of concern for the poor.

In the free world it is economic conditions that determine what kind of landowning and farming is to prevail, and not the ideas of Utopians who favour a particular kind of landowning system above all others; and it is those who are able to judge correctly what in their own lifetime is to be the form of production most likely to be needed, and are able to find the resources and skills necessary to carry it out, who will best survive.

The justification, from a national point of view, of the small agricultural freeholder is that he produces food which is required by the nation, and that in so doing he is able to maintain his family in dignity and independence.

The justification for a large farmer-landowner from that point of view is that he produces a good deal of food required by the nation on an efficient basis, gives employment to a rural population, keeps up a steady investment on his land, maintains and improves the fertility of the soil, and pioneers new methods of agricultural production. If he succeeds in doing all that, he is playing his part in that continuous movement of agricultural improvement which has so revolutionized British agriculture over the last two and a half centuries, and is following worthily in the footsteps of the great agricultural improvers of the eighteenth and nineteenth centuries.

CHAPTER *15*

Epilogue

Five years ago I might have said that, apart from an attack of gout twelve years before, I had enjoyed good health ever since I could remember, but following some blood tests at the end of 1982, I was told by a Harley Street specialist that I had a rare form of blood cancer which could kill me, if nothing else did, within an unspecified time, possibly within three months, or maybe in two or three years.

When a man in seemingly good health is suddenly told that he is soon to die, his immediate reaction is probably one of fear. I experienced that fear for a while. Suddenly it was brought home to me that I was about to leave my loved ones and all the familiar sights and sounds of existence. My daily life, my mundane hopes and expectations were soon to end, and naturally they then became inexpressibly dear to me. I felt an almost overpowering feeling of compassion for those from whom I believed I was soon to part, particularly Colette. The boys would suffer but they were young and strong and would survive, but Colette was particularly vulnerable and for her I trembled.

A further thought aroused by this desolating announcement was the realization that my potential for good and evil was almost used up, that as my life was nearing its completion, only my actions throughout life now meant anything. Any good intentions which, through weakness of will or pure laziness, had not been followed by action, now signified nothing. I began to survey my life and to judge myself, a preparation possibly for another judgement from Him from whom there is no appeal.

Meanwhile I tried to carry on my life much as before, so as to reassure my family that life for them would go on much as it had in the past. Wishing to spare them the knowledge, I did not tell them of the course of my disease as it had been told to me.

That was a foolish decision, as it turned out. For the first nine months or so after that meeting with the Harley Street specialist, there was no great deterioration in my condition, and I allowed myself to think that my disease might be so unpredictable as to spare me its consequences for longer than I had been given to expect. That Summer we went to the Mediterranean as usual during the hay-fever season, and I caught a bad stomach bug. From then on I grew steadily weaker. In December 1983 I suddenly fainted at a party given by my former law partner, Sir Hugh Rossi. Still, my doctor thought it was merely the heat and the alcohol. We went down to Ashley Chase for our usual month's stay at Christmas. There I began to lose weight rapidly and suddenly to look very old. Colette was in a panic, and we returned to London precipitately. As Roby drove us off, I looked at our house, thinking that it might possibly be the last time I should see it.

Tests followed, and to my relief and astonishment, diabetes was diagnosed. I was astonished because previous tests for it had all been negative, although I should not have been surprised since my father and all my paternal uncles had had it. It was a great relief, for the symptoms could have heralded something much worse. I went to a specialist, was given tablets and put on a diet. Colette immediately set to work to read the diet book and to weigh out the food I was allowed to eat.

Epilogue

Within two or three weeks I again registered negative to my glucose tests. My doctor, without telling my diabetic specialist what he was doing, told me to stop the tablets. About ten days later I developed a high temperature which would not go away. On the fourth day, I went into hospital, and it was not a moment too soon. I had developed septicaemia with five times the normal amount of glucose in the blood. I stayed there fifteen days, and at first it was probably touch and go whether I would survive. Two specialists, one for diabetes and the other for septicaemia, between them saved my life. But when I came to give myself a strip wash, I got a frightful shock, for I looked almost like a survivor from Belsen. It is characteristic of diabetes to strip its victims of their muscles first and then the rest of their flesh. No wonder it was once called the 'wasting disease'.

Colette sat by my side for twelve hours every day of that ordeal. Roby and Cedric came every day. On the third day I told them that, though I might be mistaken, I did not expect to die this time, but that they should regard it as a trial run. I told them what I wished them to do after I had gone. With the shock of that disclosure, they that day became men.

Recuperation was a long-drawn-out affair. In hospital I had developed an intense love for flowers. I would lie in bed watching and handling the flowers sent to me. Their scents, their colours and their intricate and various shapes held me spellbound with wonder. Now at Ashley, I could sit in the garden in the midst of daffodils and experience that wonder once more, but in a natural setting.

I began to recover from the worst effects of diabetes, but grew steadily worse from the blood disease. I became very weak and tired. I tried to grapple with the problems presenting themselves at Ashley Chase. It was the time of crisis over milk quotas, and I dealt with the matters as well as I could, but sometimes fell asleep during meetings through sheer drowsiness.

In February 1985 I went down with 'flu and in March developed bronchial pneumonia. I think that something like panic began to spread around the estate. If I was to die, what would happen to it and those who worked on it? They feared the usual break-up and dispersion which often follows the death of an owner of a sizeable business or estate, when the State steps in to plunder the inheritance.

That Spring Cedric drove me up to London, and John Thacker has since told me that he did not expect to see me again. I was going up to see a blood specialist whose name I had been given six months before but had been dissuaded from seeing by two of my doctors. Their argument had been that having seen two specialists, neither of whom had been aware of any effective treatment, I should not bother with anyone else. Nevertheless, I finally went.

To my utter astonishment I learnt from Dr Grant Prentice of the Royal Free Hospital in Hampstead that my blood disease was not a cancer, but simply a serious condition which, over the previous four or five years, had been successfully treated in others with chemotherapy. He had over a dozen patients whom he had been treating and they were all doing well and leading reasonably normal lives. Of course one had to start in time, before one's enlarged spleen had come to occupy most of one's stomach and interfere with the other organs, but subject to that, he had never had a failure. There was no reason why, if the chemotherapy worked, since I was very healthy apart from the blood disease and the diabetes, I should not survive another twenty years or more.

That sounded somewhat extreme to me. 'Do you think that I'll see my seventieth birthday in some vigour?' I asked. 'That is what we aim at,' he replied. I came away amazed, the seeds of hope beginning to fill my mind. I had been living for the previous two and a quarter years under the impression that my remaining lifespan was exceedingly limited, and my growing weakness, loss of weight and pallor only reinforced that impression. Now I was told that I should at least live the average three score and ten years of which the Psalmist writes, if not longer.

That April, I started treatment. Within six or seven weeks I noticed that my spleen was shrinking. Within three months I was almost back to what I had been three years before, full of energy, recovered weight and with a good colour. When this happened I made a point of going all round the estate, dealing with any problems as they arose, and initiating new ventures. In this way I hoped to reassure everyone that I was going to be with them for some time yet.

When I had lain in hospital drowsily surveying the outlines of my past life, its main achievements passed before me, and I knew that the creation of the Ashley Chase estate had not been the least of them. I reckoned that I had been blessed that such a large proportion of my life had been given to such a satisfying and worthwhile achievement.

I did not want that achievement to disintegrate at my death. It is a natural human instinct to attach oneself to causes, institutions and ideas that do not die with oneself. It may be that one's instinct for survival is partly satisfied that way. I knew that I had not built up the Ashley Chase estate for it to last simply for my lifetime; I wanted it carried on by my sons and their sons so that it would remain a permanent feature of the Dorset countryside.

An event had taken place some time before which made this more likely. Both Roby and Cedric had spent a good deal of their youth on the estate and loved it. Neither had developed into the hunting, fishing and shooting types which might have been expected of young men in their position. Instead, both had spent a lot of time working on the estate, either helping to get the harvest in, or making cheese in the cheese dairy. Both knew many of the men, with whom they had worked quite well. It could be said that while Roby was more socially involved with them, Cedric involved himself a bit more with their work. Roby seemed more urban-based. He had trained as an architect and after a while had set up his own partnership. Cedric had gone in a different direction. He had managed a good degree at Imperial College in electrical engineering, and followed it up with some worthwhile work with the Standard Telephone Company in their development of a marine radio relying on satellite signals, which was later installed on the *QE2* and on the Royal Yacht *Britannia*, among other ships. It was not all that clear, however, that he would relish the life of a boffin permanently.

One day we took a walk together up Wears Hill on Far Van Diemens field with Ginnie. It was a glorious morning in early Summer. The sun shone bright, birdsong was in the air, and there was not a cloud in the sky. We rested for a time on the crest of the hill as Ginnie scampered about. A mile away we could see the sunlight shining on our house, embowered in its woods like a castle from some fairy story, and two miles beyond it we could see the fourteenth-century tower of Litton Cheney's parish church sheltering under the protection of Askerswell Down. It was a dream-like scene, lovely beyond description.

I turned to Cedric and said, 'You've been lucky so far, having been brought up in a place like this. Even an exceptionally successful man in commerce or industry, if he had not had the luck to inherit such a place, would normally only be able to buy an estate like this towards the latter part of his life, and you've virtually grown up here. Don't you think it would be a worthwhile occupation to run this estate one day? There is plenty of scope for innovation, new ventures and intensification of production. And can you imagine a lovelier setting as you go about your work, and retire for the night? I daresay you like the work you are doing, but if ever there comes a time when the life and work of a research engineer begins to lose its attraction for you, I want you to remember that there is a place for you here.'

For a year or so nothing more was said about it. Much as I would have liked him to change his job, I realized that it was no use pushing him to do so, for the impetus would have to come from him. After two years he left the Standard Telephone Company when he saw the scientific work done there begin to run down. He had begun to realize that the original work of many electrical-engineering factories in Britain, particularly those owned by foreign companies, was done abroad. British factories were increasingly devoted to assembly, since conditions for work and investment were much more favourable overseas.

One day, out of the blue, he said to me, 'Is that job at Ashley Chase still available?' I said it was but that if he took it, I did not want him to do an existing man's work on a tractor, in a dairy or in the cheese dairy. 'You'll have to build up something new on the estate for which you alone will have responsibility,' I said. 'Meanwhile you had better go to a farming college for a year or so.'

By luck, he was admitted to Wye College in Kent, one of the leading agricultural colleges in the country, and took an MSc degree course in farming management. The course did not exhaust his energies, and while still there he began to build up an export business for the cheese we were making. Soon Ashley Chase Cheddar was being eaten on passenger aircraft including Concorde, on cruise ships, in Switzerland and in America. While still at college he exported about twenty tons of our cheese abroad. When he emerged with his degree and settled at Ashley, this rose to sixty and seventy tons annually. It does not sound much, but it involved a lot of trail-blazing work, intricate packing and oceans of forms to fill in. It meant a lot for our cheese dairy because it was a permitted way to exceed our datum, and it involved a 12 per cent increase in it. He also sold our Dorset Blue Vinny in London and elsewhere for as long as we manufactured it. He became an effective sales manager for our cheese and butter production, and by mid-1986, all cheese sales were under his control and were being made direct from the estate without the intervention of the Farmhouse Cheesemakers Association.

One day Watergate House, next to Kingston Russell House, appeared on the market. I bought it, and with Brian Metcalfe Jackson's help, Cedric was soon stylishly installed in it. There, on the banks of the Bride, he was in the very middle of the estate. Everyone soon began to realize that the estate was not going to disintegrate when I died, but would continue, God willing, to the next generation and to the next.

Full of energy and renewed hope that Autumn of 1985, I decided to reverse the diminution of milk production caused by milk quotas, and promptly bought 500,000 litres (110,000 gallons) of milk quota. That put us back in the position we had been in some two years before. It seemed an odd thing that we had to pay for the privilege of buying back the right to produce the milk we had been producing earlier, but it was no use lamenting the fact; it was one of the rules of the game, and if I wanted to remain a substantial player in that game, there was nothing for it but to plunge forward. I had realized that if one could survive the imposition of dairy quotas, one had in fact become a member of a cosy monopoly. There would be the usual ups and downs of any trade, but one would be part of a home industry supplying a basic food whose viability no government could afford to endanger. A self-sufficient undertaking like Ashley Chase, producing its own basic food product, and then manufacturing it into a food which had a shelf life of twelve months and more, and selling it all from there, was a viable enterprise in almost any conceivable economic scenario.

The farming interest is not immune to further blows levelled at it to cut over-production in the Common Market. This is a new phenomenon inasmuch as it coincides with British insufficiency in temperate-grown foods. The present situation can therefore be seen as a replay of that obtaining in the late nineteenth century, with France, Holland, Eire and Germany playing the role formerly played by the United States, Argentina and the old Dominions. This time, however, the brake on a prices slump will probably be applied by our Continental partners who will not be prepared to allow their farming sector to collapse. Nor is it beyond the realm of possibility that one day Britain will be able to renegotiate the farming provisions of the Common Market Treaty in favour of nations that are not self-sufficient in various foods.

There will undoubtedly be limitations on food production, either through quotas, price reductions or schemes to compensate farmers for putting land out of cultivation. I suppose that a lowering of cereal prices will partly compensate dairy farmers for a cut in production, because cattle-feed will become cheaper. If one dares to peer into the crystal ball and prognosticate about the future, one might hazard the guess that the efficient farmer on good land with the economics of a large-scale enterprise will weather the storm reasonably well, but that those on marginal soil who are also under-capitalized or over-borrowed will give up.

Future prosperity might well lie in part in the successful

exploitation of new or forgotten foods. For some time I have considered how best we might use our whey. It amounts to approximately 90 per cent of the milk which we turn into cheese, and yet we make next to no economic use of it.

One new venture which we did get off the ground in 1986 was the formation of a goats' milk production unit. We had decommissioned one of our dairies, that at Higher Kingston Russell, as a result of the imposition of milk quotas for cows' milk, and were considering to what use to put it. The obvious one, which we tried for a year, was to fatten beef cattle, but that was shown to be only marginally profitable. One day Cedric said to me, almost in jest, 'What about goats?' I did not dismiss the idea out of hand. 'Let us read up about it,' I said, 'and see if there is a market for goats' milk.' John Thacker and I did the reading and Cedric explored the market. He found that Lubborn Cheese just over the border in Somerset, the successful and enterprising makers of Somerset Brie, had also decided to make goats' cheese, and were prepared to take all the goats' milk we could supply provided it met their requirements. One not inconsiderable advantage of this venture would be that it was entirely outside the sphere of the Milk Marketing Board and, so far at any rate, beneath the notice of the Brussels bureaucracy. There was a completely free market in it without quotas or interference of any kind, provided the milk was clean.

Goats have always been superseded by cows as countries become more prosperous and agricultural land is improved. They are then driven to pasture in the mountains, in which they can thrive where almost no other livestock can. So I was contemplating quite an innovation to bring them in to replace a cow herd.

To John's and Cedric's surprise, I told them some time in May 1986, 'Let's go in for goats, provided it's in a big way.' So John began to scour the country for goats. Some were picked up in Yorkshire, some in East Anglia, some in Devon and some in Wales. We bought in several breeds, British Saanen, Anglo-Nubian, British Toggenburg, and British Alpine. By September 1986 we had installed a goat-milking parlour at Higher Kingston Russell to milk three dozen goats at a time, and were milking ninety goats in all. By the end of 1986 we had 300 goats, of which 130 were being milked.

In February 1987 we had a stroke of luck that gave us 220 of the best breeding-stock of goats in the country. The British Livestock Association selected a collection of livestock, including cows, pigs and goats which were being prepared for export to China. They had been picked with care from all over the country and were subject to every form of vaccination and test to ensure that they were free from disease. A consignment of pigs from the British Livestock Association was dispatched to China, from which the Chinese expected to improve their own breeds. To everyone's surprise, on arrival in China these animals were alleged to be suffering from foot and mouth disease, and were promptly slaughtered. The Chinese government then cancelled the contract and left the British Livestock Association with hundreds of the best and most tested livestock in the country, including 220 goats. The moment I read about this in the newspaper, I instructed John to bid for them and we got the whole flock for £18,480. I was not worried about the foot and mouth scare. It was pretty obvious that the Chinese government had run short of foreign currency, and in the usual Marxist fashion, had fabricated this story to cover up their weakness.

By August 1987, with over 700 goats we had what was probably the largest flock in the country. I aimed at a flock of 1,000 by the end of the year and envisaged eventually having at least 1,000 milkers. These goats, with their engaging ways, soon became the most popular livestock on the estate, and everyone wanted to have a try at milking them.

In the Summer of 1987, Cedric made another suggestion. 'Why not go in for milking sheep and making ewes' cheese?' Our previous experience with sheep had been unprofitable, but this venture would be different. It would involve perhaps 500 ewes, who would be housed during lactation, and the product would, if we were lucky, be a relatively high-priced food for which there was a growing demand. Another advantage was that this would be one more enterprise free of the restraining hand of the Milk Marketing Board. So we have put in hand investigations, and I do not doubt that before very long we shall be making brebis cheese, as the French call it, from our own flock.

Finally, we have been allowed to buy in milk for cheesemaking after having been denied it for fifteen years. So we expect to be making 850 tons of cheese this year, and within a year or two increasing that to 1,400 tons, of which our own milk will provide half. Thus, within two or three years of the imposition of milk quotas, a move designed to make farming less profitable for dairy farmers and one which certainly contributed towards thousands of them leaving dairying altogether, we find ourselves expanding our enterprise and making it more profitable than ever before. Necessity is the mother of invention and often provides the impetus for success.

After twenty years of endeavour on a long and adventurous road, it would be natural for anyone to look back and to consider what he has done. It inevitably gives rise to certain questions, among which are: why I did it, and whether it was worth doing.

I did it for a variety of reasons which grew with the passage of time. It was for me a novel and attractive kind of enterprise in which to involve myself. The beauty of the countryside of hills and valleys under which my endeavours took place was like a magnet to me. I liked the people I was involved with. Nor did the problems which I found and had to surmount daunt me. The whole enterprise, as it grew, constantly appealed to certain instincts which are strong in me, those which prompt me to pour my energy into building up, organizing and expanding in a sphere that seems unproductive and decayed. Moreover, I found it profoundly satisfying to bring a substantial part of the countryside into maximum production and inject new life into the community living on it.

I came into agriculture at a reasonably good time, when farming was just beginning to take a new leap forward in production and profitability as a result of fresh improvements made to farming equipment and dairies and better techniques of grass management and grass conservation, and I found myself in the forefront of those utilizing these new techniques in Dorset. I was also lucky enough to turn to farming in time to foresee and to take advantage of Britain's entry into the Common Market, with all the benefits and opportunities that ensued to British agriculture from that event.

There was also something about this venture which appealed to a certain feeling of defiance to the spirit of the age which I have developed over the years. I grew up at a time when Britain was still considered a great power and regarded by its people as the hub of the civilized world, and have lived to see it decline into a third-rate economic and military power. It is a strange paradox, but the forty-odd years since the end of the Second World War which have, through the industrial and capitalist process, seen such a tremendous improvement in the material standards of life for the poorer classes, have also witnessed an accelerated decline in the standards of ethics, behaviour, speech, literature, the arts and government.

These symptoms of decline, whose origins can be traced to the late Victorian period, are, I believe, intricately connected with a decline in religious belief and the development of mass democracy. A spirit of decadence has swept over our country and filled every nook and cranny of our national culture. It is so all-embracing that many are won over to its insidious influence without being aware of its deleterious nature. Others, among whom I count myself, are so opposed to the defeatist and passive response to the centralized direction of our lives, and to the clownish and brutal sub-culture that overwhelms so many of our people, that there is bred in us a sense of alienation towards the kind of country that Britain is becoming.

To possess a landed estate gives such a man an opportunity partly to cut loose from this atmosphere of dependent helplessness which pervades the modern world. One can, to a degree, ignore some of the constraints of the modern State, the all-pervading mediocrity of thought which the media disseminate, and the tawdriness of life with which living in big cities starkly confronts us.

Here, on one's own estate, one can make an individual assessment of future trends in agricultural production, and put one's shirt on one's judgement. Here, more than in most fields, one can exert one's own individuality. One can venture to defy the enervating conformity to a pattern of decadence. Here one can show one's spirit, one's strength, one's resilience. Here one can be creative, and one can succeed.

Finally, I am a man very much rooted in the past. I may make use of all the means of production which modern industry and scientific knowledge can provide, but I use it to create for myself and for those around me a more or less traditional pattern of life. My mind is rooted in the nineteenth century and like so many people of that time, saturated with Biblical ideas and images. There is therefore nothing so satisfying to me as a life lived under the northern equivalent of one's vine and one's fig tree. The rural life, living in the midst of one's fields and one's cattle, surrounded by one's family, one's work-people and their families, and amidst all those who derive a livelihood from the land, seems to me to be the most natural and satisfying of any. And that, with all the most modern methods of production and the modern aids to living, is what I succeeded in having.

I acknowledge that the aim was unusual for anyone living in a small, modern, industrialized country whose prevailing ethos has come to include so much that is shallow and meretricious. I could not but be aware that I was swimming against the tide, and going full tilt against the 'spirit of the age' in which I lived. Despite that, I succeeded in my aims more than I dared hope. My ambition grew with the passage of time and the experience born of difficulties overcome, and eventually I came to realize that I had achieved results far greater than any I had envisaged when I first started out on this adventure.